WITHDRAWAL
UTSA LIBRARIES

D0031260

RENEWALS: 691-4574

DATE DUE

APR 2 0			
MAY 0 9			
GAYLORD			PRINTED IN U.S.A.

Human Fertility

and Population Problems

Proceedings of the Seminar Sponsored
by The American Academy of Arts and Sciences
with the support of the Ford Foundation

edited by **ROY O. GREEP**

SCHENKMAN PUBLISHING COMPANY, INC.

CAMBRIDGE, MASSACHUSETTS

LIBRARY
The University of Texas
At San Antonio

Copyright © 1963

SCHENKMAN PUBLISHING COMPANY, INC.
CAMBRIDGE 38, MASSACHUSETTS

Printed in the United States of America

LIBRARY OF CONGRESS CATALOG CARD NUMBER: 63–23151

All rights reserved. This book, or parts thereof, may not be reproduced
in any form without written permission of the publishers.

CONTENTS

LIST OF PARTICIPANTS

Dr. B. K. Adadevoh, *Massachusetts General Hospital*

Mr. M. M. Afzal, *Harvard School of Public Health*

Dr. D. T. Armstrong, *Harvard School of Dental Medicine*

Dr. E. B. Astwood, *New England Center Hospital*

Mr. H. R. Atkinson, *Brookline, Massachusetts*

Dr. U. K. Banik, *Worcester Foundation for Experimental Biology*

Dr. Joseph J. Barlow, *Boston Lying-in Hospital*

Dr. R. N. Basu, *Harvard School of Public Health*

Miss Margaret Beard, *Wellesley College*

Miss Patricia Berger, *Wellesley College*

Dr. Warren Berggren, *Boston, Massachusetts*

Mrs. Warren Berggren, *Boston, Massachusetts*

Mr. William F. Bernet, *College of the Holy Cross*

Dr. Gabriel Baily, *Worcester Foundation for Experimental Biology*

Dr. Charles R. Botticelli, *Biological Laboratories, Harvard University*

Rev. Carroll J. Bourg, *Boston College of Arts and Sciences*

Dr. Ann Brace, *Vincent Memorial Hospital*

Dr. Jack Bresler, *Biology Department, Boston University*

Miss Evelyn Barbara Celler, *Simmons College*

Dr. M. C. Chang, *Worcester Foundation for Experimental Biology*

Dr. R. A. Chieri, *Worcester Foundation for Experimental Biology*

Dr. Ansley J. Coale, *Professor of Economics and Director, Office of Population Research, Princeton University*

Mr. Peter Y. Comay, *Brandeis University*

Dr. B. K. Davis, *Worcester Foundation for Experimental Biology*

Mr. H. S. Dhillon, *Harvard School of Public Health*

Mr. Jared Diamond, *Harvard University*

Mr. Alvin Dorse, *Brown University*

Dr. Robert M. Dowben, *Massachusetts Institute of Technology*

Dr. Cora A. Du Bois, *Zemurray-Stone-Radcliffe Professor of Anthropology, Harvard University*

Mrs. Mildred Ellett, *Boston University*

Dr. Lewis L. Engel, *Associate Professor of Biological Chemistry, Harvard Medical School; Member, Committee on Arrangements for the Seminar*

Dr. Theodore Fainstat, *Free Hospital for Women*

Miss Evelyn S. France, *Worcester Foundation for Experimental Biology*

Dr. Ronald Freedman, *Professor of Sociology, University of Michigan*

Dr. Louis Fridhandler, *Worcester Foundation for Experimental Biology*

Dr. C. R. García, *Senior Scientist, Worcester Foundation for Experimental Biology; Chief, Infertility Clinic, Massachusetts General Hospital; Member, Committee on Arrangements for the Seminar*

Dr. Sumner Gochberg, *Free Hospital for Women*

Dr. M. Goodman, *Dept. of Physiology, Harvard Medical School*

Dr. Donald Goss, *Free Hospital for Women*

Dr. Seymour Gray, *Peter Bent Brigham Hospital*

Dr. Roy O. Greep, *Professor of Anatomy and Dean, Harvard School of Dental Medicine; Chairman of the Committee on Arrangements for the Seminar*

Dr. John V. Grover, *Free Hospital for Women*

Mr. John P. Hackett, *College of the Holy Cross*

Dr. Nobuyoshi Hagino, *Worcester Foundation for Experimental Biology*

Mrs. Heather Duram Halsey, *Simmons College*

Dr. Oscar Harkavy, *Associate Director, Program in Economic Development and Administration, The Ford Foundation; Member, Committee on Arrangements for the Seminar*

Dr. Arthur T. Hertig, *Professor of Pathology, Harvard Medical School*

Dr. M. Hirai, *Worcester Foundation for Experimental Biology*

Dr. Frederick L. Hisaw, *Fisher Professor of Natural History, Emeritus, Harvard University*

Dr. Hugh Robert Holtrop, *Beth Israel Hospital*

Dr. Hudson Hoagland, *Executive Director, Worcester Foundation for Experimental Biology; Research Professor of Physiology, Boston University Graduate School; President, American Academy of Arts and Sciences; Member, Committee on Arrangements for the Seminar*

Dr. Wei Huang, *Harvard Medical School*

Mr. Sayid Husain, *Boston University*

Mr. Robert B. Jessen, *Brown University*

Mr. Solomon Katz, *Northeastern University*

Mr. Daniel S. Kemp, *Harvard University*

Dr. Melvin Ketchel, *Biology Dept., Boston University*

Mr. Robert Kretsinger, *Massachusetts Institute of Technology*

Mr. Edward O. Lauman, *Harvard University*

Dr. Donald Layne, *Worcester Foundation for Experimental Biology*

Dr. Louis Levin, *Dean of Science, Brandeis University*

Mr. John J. Macisco, *Brown University*

Dr. P. Malhotrra, *Harvard School of Public Health*

Mr. Parker G. Marden, *Brown University*

Dr. John Marston, *Worcester Foundation for Experimental Biology*

Miss Mary Veronica Mason, *Emmanuel College*

Dr. E. Matsuyama, *Worcester Foundation for Experimental Biology*

Mr. Richard D. Mayer, *Brandeis University*

Dr. Janet McArthur, *Massachusetts General Hospital*

Mr. Victor McElheney, *Harvard University*

Mr. Edward Noel McIntosh, *Harvard Medical School*

Mr. William Michelson, *Harvard University*

Dr. M. S. Mounib, *Worcester Foundation for Experimental Biology*

Miss Elizabeth Murphy, *Emmanuel College*

Dr. Aloys Naville, *Rock Reproductive Clinic*

Dr. Warren O. Nelson, *Formerly Medical Director, The Population Council Inc., Rockefeller Institute for Medical Research*

Mr. Donald P. Nierlich, *Massachusetts Institute of Technology*

Mrs. Donald P. Nierlich

Miss Jane L. Noble, *Simmons College*

Mr. Ronald L. Nuttall, *Harvard University*

Mr. Patrick M. Palivena, *College of the Holy Cross*

Dr. A. S. Parkes, *Marshall Professor of the Physiology of Reproduction, University of Cambridge*

Dr. Alexander Parthenis, *Worcester Foundation for Experimental Biology*

Miss Donna Marie Perrow, *Emmanuel College*

Dr. Gregory Pincus, *Research Director, Worcester Foundation for Experimental Biology; Member, Committee on Arrangements for the Seminar*

Dr. Stephen Plank, *Harvard School of Public Health*

Dr. Suraj Prakash, *Dept. of Gynecology, Massachusetts General Hospital*

Miss Mildred A. Reardon, *Northeastern University*

Dr. Alistair Renwick, *Massachusetts General Hospital*

Dr. Elliott Rivo, *Rock Reproductive Clinic*

Dr. John Rock, *Clinical Professor of Gynecology, Emeritus, Harvard Medical School; Director, Rock Reproductive Clinic, Inc.; Member, Committee on Arrangements for the Seminar*

Mrs. Allyn H. Rule, *Boston University*

Dr. Hilton A. Salhanick, *Beth Israel Hospital*

Mr. S. Sarkar, *Massachusetts Institute of Technology*

Dr. Y. Sawada, *Worcester Foundation for Experimental Biology*

Miss Ann Schaumburg, *Wellesley College*

Mr. Surinder Sehgal, *Harvard Botanical Museum, Harvard University*

Rev. Walter Shea, S.J., M.A., *Holy Cross College*

Mr. Joel B. Sheffield, *Brandeis University*

Dr. Robert F. Slechta, *Biology Dept., Boston University*

Dr. J. C. Snyder, *Dean, Harvard School of Public Health*

Mr. Joseph Speidel, *Harvard Medical School*

Miss Ellen M. Stahle, *Northeastern University*

Mr. Volney J. Strefflre, Jr., *Harvard University*

Dr. Somers H. Sturgis, *Peter Bent Brigham Hospital*

Dr. Phillip G. Sullivan, *New England Center Hospital*

Dr. Mary Taylor, *Department of Zoology, Wellesley College*

Dr. Christopher Tietze, *Director of Research, National Committee on Maternal Health, Inc.*

Miss Linda Twombly, *Simmons College*

Dr. Geoffrey R. Venning, *G. D. Searle & Co., Ltd., England*

Miss Elizabeth Voegtlin, *Northeastern University*

Dr. A. Watanabe, *Worcester Foundation for Experimental Biology*

Miss Karen Weisskopf, *Radcliffe College*

Dr. John B. Wyon, *Assistant Professor of Population Studies, Harvard School of Public Health; formerly Field Director, India-Harvard Population Study; Member, Committee on Arrangements for the Seminar.*

Dr. H. Wyss, *Worcester Foundation for Experimental Biology*

Dr. Chei Yanagima, *Worcester Foundation for Experimental Biology*

Dr. K. Yoshinaga, *Worcester Foundation for Experimental Biology*

Miss Rose Marie Zoino, *Emmanuel College*

Dr. Henry Vaillant, *Boston City Hospital*

FOREWORD

The present volume contains the proceedings of a seminar on Human Fertility and Population Problems held under the auspices of the American Academy of Arts and Sciences in Brookline, Massachusetts, May 3 through 5, 1963.

The magnitude of the problems arising from an unprecedented multiplication of the human species has stirred the concern of thinking peoples everywhere. The expansion in world population projected for even the remainder of this century is staggering. Much attention has been devoted over past decades to trends in national and world population but the approach, until the past few years, has been mainly analytical. In the natural course of events the population projections made by students of this subject are of such accuracy as to suggest that the results are destined by immutable forces. That such an attitude of fateful resignation is unwarranted has been amply demonstrated in some areas of the world during the postwar period by the exercise of a measure of control of human fertility or fecundity.

The dominant motive in holding this seminar was to focus attention on what can be done about the population problem and how. Complete coverage of the many facets of so vast a topic was clearly not feasible. Political, religious and humanistic aspects were not dealt with. Primary consideration was given to material from the bio-medical, socio-economic and cultural fronts. Meeting with the experts in these areas were approximately one hundred students and junior staff from thirty-two institutions of higher learning in the Boston-Worcester-Providence area. It was hoped that they might profit from this experience and that perhaps some will be stimulated to contribute to the solution of these problems that everywhere haunt man's contemplation of his society in the world of tomorrow.

The papers are published in the form in which they were presented at the seminar; the discussion, however, has been edited freely by the discussants and myself, without significant alteration in substance.

It is a pleasure to acknowledge the appreciation of the committee for the fine cooperation received from each and every contributor in the assemblage and preparation of this material for publication. We are also much indebted to the publisher for expediting the publication of this volume.

ROY O. GREEP, Editor

Boston, Massachusetts
November, 1963

I

PREFATORY REMARKS

Hudson Hoagland Ph.D.

President, The American Academy of Arts and Sciences

On behalf *of the American Academy of Arts and Sciences it is a pleasure to welcome you to this Seminar on Fertility and Population Problems. These meetings have been planned by a committee made up of Dr. Roy O. Greep, chairman, Drs. Lewis Engel, Celso-Ramón García, Oscar Harkavy, Gregory Pincus, John Rock, John Wyon, and myself, and we are indebted to the Ford Foundation for a grant to the Academy that has made it possible for us to be here.*

The field of the physiology of fertility and its control has been a curiously neglected one compared to other branches of the medical sciences. This is reflected, for example, by expenditures of the National Institutes of Health of trivial sums for research compared to other branches of the medical sciences. Thus, in 1961, only about $6 million was spent in the United States, of which more than half was from pharmaceutical laboratories for development work, and only $1.3 million by the National Institutes of Health for basic research. The contrast between the $1.3 million spent on research relevant to fertility control to the $880 million spent by this agency at the same time on death control is a sad commentary on one of the most serious diseases

1

ever confronted by man. But there are signs of changing attitudes.

Within the last year, after a decade of a few voices crying in
the wilderness, there has been an awakening to the seriousness
of the population explosion. President Kennedy wisely faced
the issue as his predecessor did not. An Administration policy
statement in December said the United States "can help other
countries, upon request, to find potential sources of information
and assistance on the ways and means of dealing with population
[increases]." At a recent news conference Mr. Kennedy supported increased research in fertility and reproduction and
agreed that the information should be made available to interested nations and peoples. A report of the National Institutes of
Health, first suppressed, was later released. The National Academy of Sciences has recently come out with strong endorsement
for our government to aid governments of other countries who
desire assistance in problems of population control. After all,
this is the least we can do since reduction of death rates by
Western medicine and public health is the primary cause of the
population explosion. The recent excellent book by John Rock
entitled *The Time Has Come* has received widespread favorable
publicity, and finally in recent years leaders of the Catholic
church have come to realize the gravity of the population problem and the importance of family planning and control, although
they still insist that this control must utilize church-approved
methods which are biologically very inefficient, but hopefully
improvable by research.

As a result of prudery about sex, and of religious and political opposition to birth control, investigators have not been
encouraged to enter the very important field of mammalian
reproduction. There are many basic unanswered questions about
the physiology of reproduction which we will discuss during
this seminar.

This Seminar brings together a group of undergraduate, predoctoral and post-doctoral students with a group of outstanding investigators, to consider problems of fertility and those resulting from the population explosion. We have the hope that some of the participants in the Seminar, or some of those who read the Proceedings when they are published, will be stimulated and ultimately wish to make careers in this field — especially so since now the magnitude of the problems is becoming increasingly recognized and corresponding financial support is becoming increasingly available. We have the conviction too that all those involved in work in the population field will find in the written record of these meetings much that is of value. For we believe that these papers present the latest and most accurate information available.

CYBERNETICS OF

POPULATION CONTROL

HUDSON HOAGLAND

Executive Director, Worcester Foundation for Experimental Biology, Research Professor of Physiology, Boston University Graduate School, and President, American Academy of Arts and Sciences.

THERE IS AMBIVALENCE about many scientific discoveries. It is ironical that man's most humane motives, supported by applications of advances in medicine and public health since World War II in underdeveloped countries, are primarily responsible for the population explosion and its accompanying grave dangers. In the next two or three days we shall discuss this problem and its demographic, economic and political aspects, and hear about research in the biology of fertility and its control. At this Session, I would like to limit my remarks primarily to some of the ways in which nature deals with over-crowding in animal societies.

In multiplying cultures of microorganisms the growth rate accelerates exponentially, but as toxic metabolic products, such as acids or alcohol, accumulate, the rate declines and the curve describing numbers of organisms as a function of time ultimately flattens off. These S-shaped growth curves for microorganisms have been described by equations aimed at elucidating the dynamics of such population growths.

There are many studies on the regulation of insect populations. Thus, it has been shown that the fruit fly, *Drosophila,* above certain population densities decreases its egg laying, and to an amount proportional to the density. Many investigations have been made of flour beetles. Below a fixed number of grams of flour per beetle, cannibalism occurs in some species, egg production drops off, and in one species crowding results in females puncturing and destroying some of the eggs they have produced. Frequency of copulation also declines with crowding. There are some species of flour beetles with glands that produce a gas, the release of which is increased with crowding. This gas is lethal to larvae and acts as an antaphrodisiac at high densities of population. Flour contaminated with beetle excrement inhibits egg production of one species of beetle investigated, and mixing of this contaminated flour with fresh flour decreases the rate of population growth which is entirely reversible in the presence of fresh flour. In such cases there is ample food supply.

Among populations of mammals other than man, it was long thought that food and predators were the controlling factors in limiting populations of hares, lemmings, and other rodents, deer, caribou, and other forms. The predators might be lynxes, wolves, foxes or birds of prey, or microorganisms producing epidemic diseases. It was thought, for example, that the four-year cycles of build-up and decline of lemming populations, terminating in their suicidal migrations, were due to an increase in predators accompanying population growth which ultimately caused the panic and decline. But the migrations and deaths appear now not to be caused by the predators. Rather, the predators appear to multiply in response to the multiplying prey. While the lemming cycles have not been studied as systematically as some other species, it seems likely that these four-year fluctuations in population densities are determined by factors now known to regulate population cycles in other mammalian species, and I would now like to say something about these factors.

In past years the jack rabbit population of Minnesota has been studied extensively. These populations rise and fall through cycles of several years' duration. There is a build-up followed by a dying off. Why do these marked oscillations in numbers of rabbits occur? It was observed that when the animals died off there was usually plenty of food — they didn't starve. There were no evidences of an excessive number of predators. Furthermore, the bodies showed no sign of any specific epidemic that killed them. To quote from a 1939 study of the dead animals: "This syndrome was characterized primarily by fatty degeneration and atrophy of the liver with a coincident striking decrease in liver glycogen and a hypoglycemia preceding death. Petechial or ecchymotic brain hemorrhages, and congestion and hemorrhage of the adrenals, thyroid, and kidneys were frequent findings in a smaller number of animals. The hares characteristically died in convulsive seizures with sudden onset, running movements, hindleg extension, retraction of the head and neck, and sudden leaps with clonic seizures upon alighting. Other animals were typically lethargic or comatose." The adrenals were hypertrophied in some cases, and atrophied in others. Signs of liver disease, hypertension, athersclerosis and adrenal deterioration were typical of what one finds following Hans Seyle's acute stress syndrome resulting from overactivity of the pituitary-adrenal axis.

After the severe stress of winter crowding in burrows when population densities are high, it has been found in studies of rodents that there was much fighting among the males, sex drives were at a low ebb, the young were often eaten, and the females produced premature births. Susceptibility to nonspecific infections also was found, and this is another byproduct of excessive production of adrenal corticoids. After such a colony has depleted its numbers through effects of the stress syndrome, the colony then tends to build up again, and so it goes through repeated cycles of growth and decline.

There are many other examples. A pair of deer were put on an island in Chesapeake Bay about forty years ago. This is a small island of about 150 acres. The deer were kept well supplied with food. It was found that the colony grew until it reached a density of about one deer per acre. Then the animals began to die off and did so in spite of adequate food and care. Again, when these dead animals were examined there was marked evidence that the adrenal stress syndrome had been in operation. Studies have been made of the crowding of animals in the Philadelphia Zoo. It was found that in some species of animals there was a ten-fold increase in atherosclerosis under conditions of severe crowding, and there were many other symptoms characteristic of stress. John Christian of the Naval Medical Research Institute made population studies in relation to crowding of mice. In his 1950 paper in the *Journal of Mammalogy* entitled "The adreno-pituitary system and population cycles in mammals," he wrote in part: "We now have a working hypothesis for the die-off terminating a cycle. Exhaustion of the adreno-pituitary system resulting from increased stresses inherent in a high population, especially in winter, plus the late winter demands of the reproductive system, due to increased light or other factors, precipitates population-wide death with the symptoms of adrenal insufficiency and hypoglycemic convulsions."

John Calhoun at the National Institutes of Health has studied effects of crowding on rats, and I would like to describe his work in some detail. He investigated colonies of rats kept in pens at critical levels of crowding, and observed under these circumstances high infant mortality, high abortion rates, failures of mothers to build nests. The young were often scattered about and eaten. When the rats were examined there was also evidence of the stress syndrome, and Calhoun has spoken, most appropriately, of what he calls "pathological togetherness." He has reviewed this work in an article entitled "Population density and social pathology," published in the *Scientific American,* February, 1962, and the following description is an abbreviation of this paper.

Calhoun confined wild Norway rats in a one-quarter acre enclosure with plenty of food and water. At the end of 27 months the population stabilized itself at 150 adults. One would expect from the very low adult mortality rate in uncrowded conditions a population of 5000, not 150 rats. But infant mortality was extremely high. The stress from social interaction disrupted maternal behavior so that only a few of the young survived. Calhoun later studied groups of domesticated white rats confined indoors in observation rooms under better controlled conditions. Six different populations were examined. Each group was allowed to increase to twice the number that his earlier experience indicated could occupy the space allotted with only moderate stress. Pathological behavior was most marked in the females. Pregnancies were often not full term. There were many abortions and many maternal deaths. The mothers often could not nurse or care for their young. Among the males there was much sexual deviation, homosexual behavior, cannibalism, and abnormal behavior ranging from frenetic overactivity to pathological withdrawal in which some males emerged from their nests only to eat and drink. Patterns of social behavior were thus badly deranged at twice normal crowding.

The experiments took place in four interconnecting pens, each 6 x 6 feet in area. Each was a complete dwelling unit, with a drinking fountain, a food hopper and an elevated artificial burrow. The burrow was reached by a winding ramp that held five nest boxes. One of these storied rat apartment houses was located in each of the four pens. There was comfortable space in this colony for 12 adult rats in each pen, the size of the groups in which rats are normally found to thrive. The setup should thus have been able to support 48 rats comfortably without overcrowding. At the stabilized number of 80 to 100, double the comfortable population, which they were allowed to reach by breeding, an equal distribution of the animals would have found 20–25 adults in each pen, but the animals did not dispose themselves in this way.

Biasing factors were introduced in the following fashion. Ramps were arranged enabling the animals to get from one pen to another and so transverse the entire four pens in the room. However, the two end pens, Nos. 1 and 4, each had only one ramp connecting them with pens 2 and 3 respectively, while the middle pens had two ramps each, i.e., ramps connecting pen 2 with 3, and a ramp connecting pen 2 with pen 1, and a ramp connecting pen 3 with pen 4. The rats had to make a complete traverse of the pens to go from one of the end pens to the other. This arrangement of ramps immediately skewed the probabilities in favor of a higher density in the two middle pens, since pens 2 and 3 could be reached by two ramps whereas pens 1 and 4 by only one ramp each. But with the passage of time strange aspects of the behavior of the group skewed the distribution in an unexpected way. This also resulted in an unexpected arrangement of the sex ratios of the animals in the various pens. The females distributed themselves about equally in the four pens, but the male population was concentrated almost overwhelmingly in the middle pens. One reason for this was because of the status struggle which takes place among the males. Shortly after six months of age the males each enter into a round robin of fights that eventually fixes their position in the social hierarchy. These fights took place in all of the pens, both the middle and the end pens; but in the end pens it became possible for a single dominant male to take over the area as his territory during the period when the social hierarchy was being established.

Calhoun describes how this came about. The subordinate males in all pens adopted the habit of arising early. This enabled them to eat and drink in peace. Rats generally eat in the course of their normal wanderings, and the subordinate residents of the end pens, having been defeated by the dominant male in these pens, were likely to feed in one of the middle pens where they had not had as yet to fight for status. When, after feeding, they wanted to return to their original quarters, they found it very difficult to do so. By this time the dominant male in the end pen would have awakened and he would engage the subordinates in fights as they tried to come down the single ramp to the pen. For a while the subordinate would continue his efforts to return to what had been his home pen, but after a succession of defeats he would become so conditioned that he would not even make the attempt. In essence, Calhoun points out that the dominant male established his territory of domination in the end pens, and his control over a harem of females — not by driving the other males out but by preventing their return over the one ramp leading to the end pen. While the dominant male in an end pen slept a good part of the time, he made his sleeping quarters at the base of the ramp. He was therefore on perpetual guard, awakening as soon as another male appeared at the head of the ramp. He usually only had to open his eyes for the invader to wheel around and return to the adjoining pen. Since there were two ramps for pens 2 and 3, no one male could thus dominate both of them. The dominant males in pens 1 or 4 would sleep calmly through all the comings and goings of his harem. Seemingly he did not even hear them. His condition during his waking hours reflected his dominant status. He would move about in a casual and deliberate fashion, occasionally inspecting the burrow and nests of his harem. But he would rarely enter a burrow, as some other males did in the middle pens merely to ferret out the females. A territorial male might tolerate other males in his domain, provided they were phlegmatic and made themselves scarce. Most of the time these subordinate males would hide in the burrows with the adult females, and only come out onto the floor to eat and drink.

These subordinate males never tried to engage in sexual activity with the females.

In the end pens, where population density was thus kept low, the mortality rate among infants and females was also low. Of the various social environments that developed during the course of the experiments, the breed pens — as these two end pens were called — were the only healthy ones, at least in terms of survival of the group. The harem females generally made good mothers and protected their pups from harm. The pregnancy rates of the females in the middle pens were the same as those in the end pens, but a very much lower percentage of their pregnancies terminated in live births. In one series of experiments 99% of the young born in pens 2 and 3 perished before weaning, and in others of the six experiments somewhere between 80% and 95% perished. In contrast, in the two end pens infant mortality was very low.

The females that lived in the densely populated middle pens became progressively less adapted to building adequate nests, and eventually stopped building them at all. Normally rats of both sexes build nests. The females do so most vigorously around the time of parturition. It is an undertaking that involves repeated periods of sustained activity with the searching out of appropriate materials, such as strips of paper, which were made available to them, and transporting the strips to a nest which is arranged in a cup-like form. In the crowded middle pens, however, the ability of the females to persist in this activity was greatly impaired. The females began merely to pile the strips in heaps, sometimes trampling them into a pad, showing little signs of cup formation. Later they would bring fewer and fewer strips to the nesting site, and in the midst of transporting a bit of material would drop it and engage in some other activity, occasioned by contact and interaction with other rats met on the way. In the extreme disruption of their behavior during the later months of the population's history, they would build no nests at all, but would bear their litters on the sawdust in the burrow box. The females also lost the ability to transport their litters from one place to another — a thing they would normally do with skill. If they tried to move a litter, they would drop individuals and scatter them about on the floor. The infants thus abandoned throughout the pens were seldom nursed. They would die where they were dropped and were thereupon eaten by the adults. In the middle pens, when a female would come into heat, she would be relentlessly pursued by all of the males until she was exhausted. This caused death of 25% of the females in a relatively short time in the crowded pens; in contrast, only 15% of the adult males died over the same time in the middle pens. In the end brood pens, Nos. 1 and 4, however, this sort of thing didn't happen. The females in these pens would retire to bear their young in nests they made in a normal fashion, and were protected from the excessive attention of the other males by the territorial male.

In the middle pens, Nos. 2 and 3, a great deal of fighting among the males went on, with now one and now another assuming the dominant position. After a while, most of the males in the middle pens gave up this struggle and simply retired, making themselves as scarce as possible and spending a lot of time in their sleeping quarters. In contrast, in the brood pens 1 and 4, one male predominated and peace generally reigned. These dominant males took care of the females and of the juveniles, never bothering them in any way.

Among the sub-dominant males there was much abnormal behavior. For instance, there was a group of homosexuals. They were really pan-sexual animals, and apparently could not discriminate between sex partners. They made sexual advances to males, juveniles, and females that were not in oestrus. They were frequently attacked by their more dominant associates, but they very rarely contended for status.

Another type of male emerged in the crowded pens. This was essentially a very passive type that moved a good deal like a somnambulist. These ignored the other rats of both sexes and all the other rats ignored them. Even when the females were in oestrus, these passive animals made no advances to them, and only very rarely did other males approach them for any kind of play. They appeared to be healthy, attractive and sleek, but were simply zombies in their conduct as far as the other rats were concerned, never engaging in fights or showing sexual interest in the other animals.

The strangest of all of the abnormal male types, described by Calhoun, were what he called the probers. These animals, which always lived in the middle pens, took no part at all in the status struggle. Nevertheless they were most active of all the males in the experimental population, and they persisted in their activities in spite of attacks by the dominant animals. In addition to being hyperactive, the probers were hypersexual, and in time many of them became cannibalistic. They were always chasing females about, entering their nests, having intercourse with them in the nest — a thing that the normal rats would never do. These probers conducted their pursuits of oestrus females in a very abnormal manner, abandoning all courtship ritual, which is characteristic of mating rats.

From these experiments of John Calhoun at the National Institutes of Health we have seen the development of serious pathology in a society directly attributable to overcrowding at only twice the number of rats per unit area required for a healthy society.

A question of immediate interest is to what extent the stress syndrome may be a limiting factor in reducing the growth rate of human populations. As far as I know, there are no adequate data to answer this question. Studies from a number of laboratories including our own have demonstrated that the pituitary adrenal system responds under stress in a way similar to that of other mammals. There is indirect evidence that inmates of concentration camps experienced acute forms of the stress syndrome that may have accounted for many deaths. Concentration camps would be more appropriate sources of comparison to highly congested animal populations than would be city slums, since in crowded cities the very poor do have some mobility. They can escape from their immediate congestion on streets and associate with other segments of the population. The incidence of street gangs and juvenile delinquency is especially characteristic of overcrowded city areas and constitutes a form of social pathology. Several studies have also indicated a higher incidence of schizophrenia and of other psychotic and neurotic behavior in congested urban areas in contrast to more spacious surroundings, but other factors may be involved here. The increased incidence of atherosclerosis and other cardiovascular pathology associated with urban living and its competitive stresses may also be enhanced by crowding, although direct evidence for this role of population density *per se* is lacking. In underdeveloped countries with high birth rates and recently lowered death rates, producing population growths of 2 to 4 per cent per year, any growth-slowing effect of the stress syndrome would be obliterated by the use of medical and public health measures that are enhancing life expectancies and that would mask any smaller effects of decreased life expectancies resulting from stress.

There has developed a large literature on the social behavior of animals in relation to population density. V. C. Wynne-Edwards has published an important book called *Animal Dispersion in Relation to Social Behavior* (Hafner Press, New York, 1962). Let me summarize some of his conclusions.

In nature, when food supplies are fortuitously removed or fail to materialize, a local emergency of overpopulation results, and especially among highly mobile flying animals such as insects and birds this can be immediately relieved by emigration. The social hierarchy and code of behavior to which the animal subscribes acts as a device to force out whatever surplus of animals exists. The exiles may be condemned to perish or, under different circumstances, they may set up new populations in other localities. In the cold boreal and arctic regions, most of the erupting species are birds. Many birds are adapted to exploit intermittent or undependable crops of food, and are to a large extent nomadic in their search for regions where supplies are temporarily plentiful. Two distinct biological functions appear to be served by emigration. One is that of a safety valve to give immediate relief to overpopulation, and the other is a pioneering function to expand and replenish the range of the species as a whole, and provide for gene exchange. Emigration of the safety valve kind is associated with stress and with quickly deteriorating economic conditions (e.g., locusts). On the other hand, providing pioneers is something that can be afforded only when conditions are good. In more variable environments, both functions tend to become important and to be exercised on a large scale. The individuals expelled are in either case usually the junior fraction of the hierarchy.

In this connection I am reminded of human colonizing activities — the Greek city states that sent young people off to colonize the Mediterranean areas of Italy, Sicily and Africa, and the lands around the Aegean and the Black Sea. The younger sons of British families and the emigrants of Portugal, Spain and France come to mind, establishing colonies in the western hemisphere and relieving population pressures at home. Like many animal colonies, Australia was originally colonized by a group very low in the British pecking order, i.e., prisoners. Ireland is another especially interesting case. In 1670 Ireland had a population of approximately a million people. By 1845 this had increased to eight million. The Irish were heavily dependent upon only one crop — the potato, which was grown on small plots of land sufficient to feed a family. Over a period of six years (1845–1854) a blight destroyed the potato crop. About a million people starved and another million emigrated at this time. Agricultural reforms were introduced — the small plots were consolidated for purposes of diverse crop farming and primogeniture was established. But the population continued to fall, and it is now about four million — half of what it was before the potato famine. Reasons for this decline have been continued emigration and a change in habits to very late marriages and often no marriage at all. The eldest son maintains the farm, cares for his parents and usually does not marry while they are alive. The result is that population growth in Ireland is low despite the influence of the Catholic Church.

Today, human emigration on a significant scale has ceased everywhere. The frontier is no more and there are few areas that welcome immigrants in our world of intensified nationalisms.

Wynne-Edwards points out that the same general social machinery that controls safety valve emigrations is involved in regulating seasonal redispersions of animals, such as the annual two-way migrations of birds. Many studies, other than those already mentioned, of mortality promoted by stress have been made. The white stork has been intensively studied. Nestling mortality is often very heavy under crowded conditions and individual chicks may be deliberately killed and sometimes eaten by one of their parents, usually the father. This is most likely to happen where the parents are beginners or young adults, and presumably of lower social status in the pecking hierarchy. The killing off of the young in prolific breeding conditions is characteristic of a great many birds that have been investigated, as well as many mammals, and this type of killing of the young is a direct result of social stress. The killing of the young and cannibalism are known to occur quite widely in mammals; for instance, in rodents, lions, and also in primitive man. Cases of cannibalism are found in fish, spider crabs, spiders, and cases of fratricide in insect larvae of various types. *In all cases experimentally investigated, the mortality is found to be density dependent and to cease below a certain critical population density.*

Mortality from predation has also been examined. This appears to be density dependent to the extent that the prey cooperates by making its surplus members especially vulnerable to predators. The density dependent elements in predation seem to arise on the side of the prey and not on that of the predators. Because of lowered resistance to infective agents following prolonged stress, disease as a form of predation may effectively reduce excessive population. In this case a surplus of individuals predisposed to injury by their dominant fellows naturally experience a variable amount of uncontrolled mortality, and this tends to fall most heavily on the young, as yet unprotected by acquired immunity to bacterial and viral infections. Social stress can lead to casualties at all ages, both through direct and mortal combat and through stress induced disease. The victim of severe stress is likely to develop physiological disorders affecting many organs, especially the lymphatic apparatus, including the spleen and thymus; the nervous system, circulatory, digestive and generative organs; the endocrine glands. As we have seen, this is especially true of the adrenal cortex which serves an intermediary role between the stressor and the organs responding to adrenal cortical hormones. Social stress is sometimes partly physical, as when the exercise of peck-order rights leads to the infliction of wounds, or to withholding food and shelter. But, as Wynne-Edwards points out, it may be largely mental as we know in man, who in his simpler-minded states may die from the conviction that he has been bewitched. Cases are known of birds, mammals and amphibians similarly dying from non-specific injuries apparently induced by social stress.

What about man? What can we do about the world population explosion? We can, of course, do nothing and wait for the stress syndrome or for new virus to do its work. It has been said that until recently our politicians had washed their hands of the population problem but now are wringing their hands over it. We can leave our destruction to some trigger-happy dictator with a suitable stock pile of nuclear weapons, or finally we can decide on an optimal population for the world and by education and social pressure, such as tax bonuses for small families, try to see that it is not exceeded. At the present average growth of 2% per year, there will be one square yard per person of surface of the earth's entire land area 600 years hence. Population growth depends only on the difference between birth rates and death rates. Man is the only animal that can direct its own evolution. Which of these two variables will he manipulate?

Psychological prejudice, indifference and hostility are the major blocks to population limitation. We know many methods of birth control — *coitus interruptus,* jellies, douches, diaphragms, condoms, surgical procedures and "the pill" — and ongoing research will give us more and better methods. None of these are of value if people refuse their use. Among the very poor and illiterate the cost and the difficulties of use of contraceptives demand massive government aid — financial, social and educational. Prudery and politics, myth, superstition and tradition have so far rendered birth control ineffective in countries X most in need of it. and religion

Grenville Clark in a recent paper has argued that the population explosion probably cannot be controlled until the world has acquired universal and complete disarmament under world law when a substantial part of the 120 billion dollars now being spent on weaponry might, if we are wise enough, be used to raise the living standards of have-not peoples. He bases this view on the often demonstrated fact that birth control procedures are used extensively only by literate and prosperous people with hope and ambition for bettering their own lots and those of their children. The take-off point for family planning and limitation requires a critical level of education and prosperity not now found in the very poor countries.

A still more gloomy view might be that if we do not manage to disarm in a decade or so we shall probably solve the population problem by nuclear extermination. In any case, the two

* Mostly ignorance

major problems of our time — nuclear war and the population explosion — are closely linked together. Physics and the medical sciences have given all of mankind these two world-wide challenges never dreamed of by previous generations. Only by fundamental changes in our ways of thinking can these problems be solved.

II

THE BIOLOGY OF FERTILITY

A. S. PARKES, F.R.S., Ph.D., D.Sc.

CLINICAL STUDIES ON HUMAN FERTILITY CONTROL

C. R. GARCIA, M.D.

Chairman: Lewis L. Engel, Ph.D.

THE CHAIRMAN *pointed out that in their papers, Drs. Parkes and García dealt with aspects of animal and human reproductive physiology related to the broad problems of population growth and control.*

In introducing Professor Parkes, Marshall Professor of the Physiology of Reproduction, University of Cambridge, Dr. Engel referred to his "keen scientific intuition" and also to his "ability to seek out and solve important problems." Dr. Engel recalled his first meeting with Professor Parkes ("some twenty-five years ago, while on a visit to London") in his laboratory at the National Institute for Medical Research. At that time Dr. Parkes was working on the effect of sex hormones on the plumage of birds. "I was much impressed with the scientific content of his observation as well as the sheer beauty of his test object. It is this blend of keen scientific intuition with the ability to seek out and solve important problems, combined with an appreciation

21

of the aesthetics of science, that has marked his work over the years."

The introduction of Dr. Celso-Ramón García made mention of his outstanding work on the clinical testing of synthetic progestational compounds. Dr. Engel referred to Dr. García's "extraordinary new work" and presented the second speaker as the Chief of the Infertility Clinic at the Massachusetts General Hospital. Dr. García is also Senior Scientist at the Worcester Foundation for Experimental Biology.

THE BIOLOGY OF FERTILITY

A. S. PARKES

Marshall Professor of the Physiology of Reproduction, University of Cambridge.

I am always very pleased to be able to visit the U.S., to meet old friends again and to make new ones. On this occasion it is also very nice to think that the new friends will largely be young people. In giving me the invitation, Dr. Greep said that the aim of this meeting would be to combine a small proportion of gray heads with a large one of young people. I thought this was a most excellent idea and I need hardly say that for that and other reasons I jumped at the invitation to be present. May I say that it is much more stimulating to be with people who may have a future, rather than with old ones who only have a past.

I gather from looking down the list of participants that I am the only one here from overseas; whether I was the only one invited, I don't know, but in any case, I appreciate the compliment. I would like very much to take this chance, therefore, of offering my very heartiest thanks to the organizers of this seminar, to the American Academy of Arts and Sciences and also to the Ford Foundation, for the fact that I am here.

INTRODUCTION

MY THEME is the Biology of Fertility, which I take to mean the biology of fertility in mammals, and to include, of course, the control of fertility. I want to tackle this vast subject in a very general way, with the aim of promoting discussion. As a biologist, I must start with two important biological considerations. The first is that nature takes as her motto that nothing succeeds like excess. This is especially true of reproductive capacity, and as a result, any kind of animal, if able to multiply without wastage to the limit of its reproductive capacity, would in time swamp any part of the world in which it could live. This applies even to the comparatively slow-breeding mammals, and to man himself. The fact that such an inundation does not happen shows that all animal populations are kept severely in check by limiting factors, of which the important ones are food supply, disease and enemies. Translated into terms of the human race these factors are famine, pestilence and war, the traditional scourges of mankind. More than a century ago, Malthus reiterated these well-known facts and drew the conclusion that, in the absence of voluntary control of its numbers, mankind would continue to run into highly unpleasant limiting factors. This conclusion was obviously valid, but it has often been disputed. It is very easy to forget or overlook the driving force of geometrical progression. The present 2 per cent per year increase in world population represents only a fraction of the reproductive capacity of the human race but:

"Had this rate existed from the time of Christ to now, the world population would have increased in this period by a factor of about 7×10^{16}; in other words there would have been 20 million individuals in place of each person now alive, or 100 people to each square foot. If the present world population should continue to increase at its present rate of 2 per cent per year, then, within two centuries, there will be more than 150 billion people [50 times the present population]. There can be no doubt concerning the long-term prognosis. *Either the birth rate of the world must come down or the death rate must go back up.*"*

* *The Growth of World Population*, National Academy of Sciences, 1963.

MATERNAL CARE

The second biological consideration to which I must draw your attention relates to maternal care. In the course of evolution among the vertebrate animals, external fertilization has been replaced by fertilization within the body of the female, which in turn has permitted the laying of a hard-shelled egg for external incubation or the internal gestation of the embryo seen in Eutherian mammals. The essential characteristic of the mammal, however, is not the capacity for gestation, but is a further manifestation of maternal care, the possession of mammae to secrete milk for the young. Progressive increase in maternal care, associated with various degrees of paternal care, is thus a notable feature in the evolution of the higher animals, and the process may be said to have reached a peak with the appearance of the human family, in which parental care continues long after biological need for it has ended.

The appearance of parental care has had two very interesting results. The first is that the greater the care taken of each offspring, the fewer the offspring that can be dealt with. Many fish, for instance, give little or no parental care, and produce millions of young which suffer wastage so enormous that only a small proportion reach maturity. By contrast, the larger mammals can produce comparatively few young of which a substantial proportion survive. In man, the trend towards parental care in excess of biological needs has evoked a corresponding necessity to reduce fertility below biological limits.

A further effect of the development of maternal care in vertebrate animals is that the increased complexity of the reproductive processes has inevitably increased the likelihood of breakdown at some point. In other words, infertility has become not uncommon, especially in domesticated animals and man. Here then is the paradoxical problem confronting the modern family planner — to remedy the infertility of those unable to have children and to provide motivation and methods for restricting the fertility of the rest in an acceptable way. And this situation is more than academically paradoxical. The lavishing of time and money simultaneously to *remedy* the infertility of the infertile and to *limit* the fertility of the fertile is perhaps socially justifiable, but its long term genetic consequences seem to me to be in urgent need of serious consideration. Are we in fact so decreasing the survival value of fertility, and so increasing the survival value of infertility, that we are likely to produce a race of subfertile people, able to propagate themselves only with continuous medical assistance? Evidently, no categorical answer can yet be given to this question, but at least we should realize the possible consequences of current trends. There must be better ways of limiting population growth than by relying on the appearance of wholesale spontaneous infertility.

REPRODUCTIVE CYCLES

The occurrence of internal fertilization, gestation and lactation means that elaborate cycles of reproductive activity are found in the female. There are in fact three different cycles — the reproductive phase within the life-cycle, the occurrence of breeding and non-breeding seasons within the reproductive phase, and the occurrence of fertile or infertile cycles within the breeding season. In some species there may not be a restricted breeding season or it may not be sharply defined. In others, there may be one or even two sharp and clearly defined breeding seasons in the year. The question of the occurrence of a primitive breeding season in man has been much debated. In Great Britain at the present time there is a clear seasonal fluctuation in the number of births. The peak number occurs in the early spring, corresponding to conceptions in the previous summer, and the lowest number occurs in the autumn, corresponding to conceptions around February. The difference between the high and low numbers is about 15%. It may well be that this seasonal fluctuation is due to artificial causes but the same periodicity seems to have existed a century ago when such fluctuation was not likely to have been the result of family planning.

Within the breeding season the reproductive cycle in the non-pregnant female consists essentially of two phases: the follicular phase in which the Graafian follicle matures and ovulation takes place; and the luteal phase, under the influence of the corpus luteum, during which the uterus is prepared for the reception of the fertilized egg. In most animals, the obvious stage of the cycle in the non-pregnant female is oestrus, the end of the follicular phase, at which ovulation takes place and behavioral and morphological changes appear which make the female receptive to the male and facilitate coitus. In a few animals, notably the rabbit and ferret, ovulation is not spontaneous but depends on coitus, and in these and some others, if ovulation is not accompanied by fertile coitus, a period of pseudo-pregnancy supervenes.

In man and other primates the same cyclic activity occurs in the female reproductive organs but the overt emphasis is usually rather different. In most species, willingness to receive the male is not restricted to the time of ovulation and, as in man, there may be no outward manifestation of that occurrence. By contrast, during the luteal phase of the cycle following ovulation, the preparation of the uterus for the reception of the fertilized egg is extensive. In the absence of a fertilized egg, the endometrium breaks down at the end of the luteal period to an extent which results in externally visible uterine haemorrhage — that is, in menstruation. If, on the other hand, a fertilized egg reaches the uterus and becomes implanted, a signal of unknown nature stimulates the pituitary gland to activity which maintains the corpus luteum, prevents menstruation and establishes the pregnancy. A woman therefore menstruates because she does not conceive and could theoretically conceive at puberty without first menstruating. Endometrial breakdown, however, is not due merely to the decay of the corpus luteum, because bleeding from a resting endometrium at the normal cyclic interval takes place even in the absence of ovulation.

The vaginal and vulval changes during the reproductive cycle in primates, with some exceptions, are much less definite than those in the uterus. The lack of such changes in women during the menstrual cycle is one of the chief obstacles to the accurate determination of the time of ovulation. In some monkeys, by contrast, e.g., the baboon, the occurrence of ovulation can be detected within a few hours by the sudden decrease of turgidity in the enormous perivulval swelling which develops during the follicular phase.

OVARIAN HORMONES

Observations on spayed animals and ectopic grafting of ovarian tissue showed that the ovarian factor involved in control of the female reproductive tract was hormonal in nature. Before crystalline substances were prepared from the ovary, however, it was discovered that massive oestrogenic activity occurred in the urine of pregnant women and mares, and two substances were rapidly isolated — oestrone and oestriol. Oestradiol, the most active of the naturally occurring oestrogens, and oestrone were subsequently isolated from ovarian extracts. As is well known the natural oestrogens proved to be steroids closely related to cholesterol.

Somewhat similar work with extracts of the corpus luteum resulted in the isolation and characterization of progesterone. By appropriate time and dosage combinations of oestrogens and progesterone it was found possible to imitate in spayed animals all the cyclic changes taking place in the non-pregnant female.

Progesterone-like activity has also been found in a large number of artificially prepared, but related, compounds with the steroid nucleus. Unlike oestrogenic activity progestagenic activity has not been found outside this nucleus.

Much interesting work has been done in recent years on the excretion pattern in human urine during the menstrual cycle of the three oestrogens already mentioned and of pregnanediol, the excretion product of progesterone. The figures obtained are complicated by the fact that some proportion of the substances present are extra-ovarian in origin, as shown by the fact that there is a low but steady excretion of them after ovariectomy. During the luteal phase, the excretion of pregnanediol rises substantially as would be expected. Oestrone and oestriol are excreted in about similar amounts, although the biological activity of the oestrone is greater. Oestradiol has a comparatively low excretion rate. With all three however, there is, again as might be expected, a gradual rise during the follicular phase up to the presumed time of ovulation and then a decline during the early luteal phase. There is then a temporary rise of unknown cause corresponding with the peak period of pregnanediol excretion.

BIOLOGY OF THE TESTIS

Like the ovary, the testis has the dual function of producing both germ cells and hormones. Also like the ovary, it has, in many animals, a cycle associated with a breeding and non-breeding season. Unlike the ovary, however, the testis, when active, produces a continuous flood of germ cells, so that tens of thousands of millions of spermatozoa may appear in a single ejaculation of an animal such as the bull and the boar. In man, any number up to about five hundred million may be found, the minimum required for fertility being perhaps 20 million.

The fate of these enormous numbers of spermatozoa in the male or female tracts is of some interest. Normally they seem to be disposed of without ill effect, but it is possible that sometimes their antigenic components are absorbed and lead to auto- or iso-immunization, which results in otherwise inexplicable infertility in male or female. Here is a clue worthy of vigorous pursuit.

In the male reproductive tract, the spermatozoa may retain potential fertilizing power for some weeks, provided that the epithelium is maintained in an active condition by the androgenic secretions of the testis. By contrast, sperm in the female reproductive tract survive only a short period, except in very few species. Survival of spermatozoa in the human female reproductive tract probably does not exceed two or three days, so that allowing a maximum survival time of one day for the ovum, the fertile period in the human menstrual cycle is thus not more than 4 days and is probably much less. Unfortunately, the difficulty of detecting the time of ovulation accurately, especially in advance, makes it difficult to detect the exact incidence of this fertile period.

THE ANDROGENIC HORMONES

The effects of castration show that the testis is responsible not only for maintaining the integrity of the accessory reproductive organs, but also that of various secondary sexual characters such as the deep voice and the beard of the human male. Behavioral characteristics are also involved. As in the case of ovarian tissue, the restorative effects of ectopic testis grafts indicate that the effect is exerted through the action of hormones. Testis grafts differ, however, in several ways from ovarian grafts. First, they do not produce germ cells in the ectopic position, because in all experimental animals the lower temperature afforded to the testis by the scrotal position is necessary for spermatogenesis. Second, owing mainly to technical difficulties, orthotopic grafting of the gonad to restore fertility has not yet been effected in castrated males as it has been in spayed or sterilized females.

Various methods of destroying the seminiferous tubules of the testis leaving intact the interstitial Leydig cells show that the latter produce the essential androgenic hormone. The small amount of this tissue made the preparation of androgenic extracts difficult but when a highly active concentrate became available it was soon demonstrated that the operative substance, testosterone, was another of the steroid series closely related to the ovarian hormones and very similar to androsterone which had earlier been isolated from male urine.

AMBISEXUALITY

At this stage, however, the story becomes less simple. The oestrogens have no activity which can properly be called androgenic. Their effect in the male consists in keratinizing various epithelia and in causing overgrowth of fibrous tissue, neither of which are produced by testosterone. Some of the androgens, however, have substantial gynaecogenic action in that many produce growth of the uterus in the immature or ovariectomised animal similar to that caused by oestrogen, and a few show varying degrees of progestational activity. The same or similar androgens cause intense mucification of the vaginal epithelium, such as is found during the luteal phase in many animals and at least one androgenic compound produces vaginal cornification. To what extent metabolic by-products of the compounds are involved in the reactions is not known. Worse still, for those who prefer simplicity to complexity, oestrogenic activity was detected in testes and male urine before androgenic activity. Outstanding instances are the testes of the stallion and pig, which contain very large amounts of oestrogen, and human male urine in which there are oestrogens in amounts similar to those found in females. The source of the testicular oestrogens is not known for certain, but from the fact that detectable amounts of oestrogens occur in human semen it is sometimes said to be ascribed to the seminiferous tubules. The testicular oestrogens do not usually cause abnormal growth or indications of feminization in the male, but both may occur. Thus, the enlarged prostate found in old dogs almost certainly results from hyperoestrogenaemia and the type of male pseudohermaphroditism known as testicular feminization, in which an almost normal female *habitus* is found in genetic males, is apparently caused by oestrogen coming from the interstitial tissue or Sertoli cells of the cryptorchid testes found in such cases.

In the same way as there are oestrogens in the testis and in male urine, there are androgens in the ovary and in female urine. Small amounts of androgen appear to be present normally in the ovary without obvious biological effects, but under conditions of increased production or abnormal liberation ovarian androgens become overtly active, as in the case of masculinizing ovarian tumors or androgenic ovarian grafts. The urinary androgens in women, like the urinary oestrogens in men, appear from gonadectomy experiments to be derived partly from the gonad and partly from the adrenal cortex, the sex hormone activity of which is well demonstrated by the occurrence of virilizing or feminizing tumors. For a long time, these apparent anomalies were most puzzling, but they are now readily explicable by the fact that the various steroid hormones are produced by similar biosynthetic pathways, involving essentially cholesterol, progesterone, androgen and oestrogen, and differing mainly in the relative amounts of the substances produced. The effects of this biosynthesis, therefore, depend on quantitative rather than qualitative factors, and sexuality is the result of a balance of endocrine factors, not an absolute state.

THE GONADOTROPHINS

Subject to certain qualifications, it may be said that the gonad is responsible for the functional activity of the accessory reproductive organs. In turn, as realized long ago, the gonad is subject to dominating extra-gonadal influences. Thus an ovarian graft loses the somatic age of the donor and takes on the somatic age of the recipient, and compensatory hypertrophy takes place in the remaining ovary if one ovary is removed. Various clinical observations suggested that the seat of extra-gonadal control might be the anterior pituitary body and this supposition was confirmed when characteristic, if rather chaotic, changes in the ovary of hypophysectomized or immature animals were caused by implanting pituitary tissue under the skin. Experiments on hypophysectomized rats with various kinds of pituitary extract showed that at least two different hormones were involved in the regulation of the cycle-follicle stimulating hormone (FSH) responsible for bringing the follicle to the point of ovulation, and luteinizing hormone (LH) responsible with FSH for ovulation and the early development of the corpus luteum.

The preparation of active gonadotrophic extracts precipitated an orgy of work, much of it designed to investigate what types of infertility in man and domestic animals might be susceptible to gonadotrophin treatment, or to bring about the superovulation of an abnormal number of eggs and the establishment of a superpregnancy. Results in this field, on the whole, have been disappointing. It was discovered long ago that the gonadotrophins, being protein-like substances, are antigenic when injected over long periods into animals of a different species from the donor. Such animals become desensitized to the exogenous gonadotrophin and often also to their own endogenous gonadotrophin. The serum of such desensitized animals inhibits the same gonadotrophin, and often the endogenous gonadotrophins, in another animal. The basic facts of the *in vivo* reactions were studied in some detail 25 years ago by Rowlands, and in spite of much recent *in vitro* immunological work, remarkably little has since been added to our knowledge of the biological possibilities of antibodies to gonadotrophins. Gonadotrophic extracts of ox pituitary were found to evoke particularly interesting antibodies which would inhibit endogenous gonadotrophin in both the rabbit and the rat, and would alter the qualitative effect of gonadotrophic preparations from the pituitary glands of other species. The comparative neglect of this most interesting line of work is remarkable and should surely be corrected.

Turning now to the problem of improving on normal fertility by the use of gonadotrophins, it is well known that superovulation and superimplantation are easy to produce, but that outside litters rarely result. The failure of superpregnancies at an early stage seems to imply that some limiting factor steps in before metabolic or mechanical limitations become severe. This most interesting phenomenon may have some connection with the implantation feedback to the pituitary gland, and even with the observation that hysterectomy may prolong the life of the corpus luteum. Here again is a potentially fertile field for research.

Neurohumoral and Feedback Mechanisms

The discovery of the pituitary gonadotrophins did not solve the problem of gonadal control, it simply pushed it one step back from the gonad and raised the further question of what controlled the pituitary gland. A further stage has now been reached when it is known that the secretion of gonadotrophins by the pituitary gland is initiated largely by hypothalamic stimuli acting through neurohumoral channels. Such stimuli may be initiated by some internal clock, by peripheral events such as mating or ovo-implantation, or by external factors, such as social odors and increase or decrease of the length of daylight.

A further essential link in this chain of control necessary to prevent overstimulation of the gonads, is found in the fact that overproduction of the gonadal steroid hormones acts back through the hypothalamus on the pituitary gland to damp down gonadotrophin secretion. Exciting progress is now being made in elucidating the factors involved in this feedback mechanism, both as to the direct effect of the gonadal hormones on the hypothalamus, and as to the nature of the substances secreted by the hypothalamus to regulate hypophysial activity.

In a more practical context the preparation of orally active analogues of the ovarian hormones has enabled the ovarian-hypothalamus-pituitary feedback mechanisms to be utilized for the inhibition of ovulation and the control of cycle length in man, and the synchronization of oestrus in animals. So far, almost all work of this kind has been carried out with hormonally active compounds which have other effects than the inhibition of ovulation. Orally active progestagens, for instance, produce effects on the endometrium and cervical mucus which would in any case tend to inhibit conception and which probably provide second and third lines of defense in the event of breakthrough ovulation. It is of some interest, therefore, that at least one non-hormonal non-steroid compound has now been developed which appears to have no other action than the blocking of pituitary gonadotrophin output, ICI Compound 33,828.

* * *

This then is some of the basic biology upon which improved methods of fertility control in man must be based. In conclusion, I should like to add one final thought. Civilization and science have brought many specialized qualities and facilities to man, but in my opinion the possession of the will and the means consciously to adapt his fertility to his environment will distinguish man from the lower animals in a far more fundamental way than does, say, the possession of works of art and atomic bombs.

DISCUSSION

Dr. Engel declared the meeting open for discussion.

DR. TIETZE: To start on a light note, I want to refer to Dr. Parkes' last remarks dealing with the synchronization of estrus in mice. This fact has also been accomplished in the human species by John C. Cobb and his associates in a village near Lahore, Pakistan. The intention was to find out whether the regular taking of oral contraceptives could be tied to the phases of the moon. A number of women have been adjusted to an artificial menstrual cycle, all starting their medication on the same day and most of them menstruating within a day or two of each other. The sociological consequences of this arrangement have not yet been explored. The local people are used to counting time from the new moon, according to the tradition of the Muslim calendar.

DR. PARKES: If I remember rightly the idea behind this was that many of these women could not count adequately, and if they could be synchronized with the moon they wouldn't have to.

DR. TIETZE: That is correct.

DR. PINCUS: May I ask Dr. Parkes to comment on the period of sterility which is known to occur during the period of lactation. This seems to me to have many implications in the sense that the factors causing sterility during lactation may be very pertinent to the control of reproduction. In fact it is well known that in many human societies this is considered as a legitimate and normal method for controlling reproduction.

DR. PARKES: This is really a bit outside my subject but I think Dr. Tietze probably can answer your question much better than I can, and I hope he will. As I understand the matter, after parturition the ovary gradually resumes activity. The endometrium goes into a gradually increasing proliferative phase and then the next thing that happens is menstruation at the end of an anovular cycle and then after perhaps two anovular cycles ovulation again starts and the fertility is restored. But the time sequels of those events varies enormously according to whether lactation is being maintained particularly and also according to race and climate and other things. But there are better authorities here than I am on this subject.

DR. TIETZE: I can comment from the statistical point of view but not from that of endocrinology. As we all know, some women do conceive in postpartum amenorrhea so it is quite obvious that in some instances the first postpartum cycle is ovulatory. If a woman ovulates prior to what would have been the first menstrual period and if she is exposed to the risk of conception, she may conceive at this first ovulation and not menstruate at all between pregnancies. This sequence of events is comparatively rare. Statistics on this point are not very good but it would seem that without birth control conception in amenorrhea occurs in about 5 per cent of the intervals. Prolonged lactation is associated statistically with prolonged amenorrhea. While some women start menstruating before they stop breastfeeding, the statistical association nevertheless exists. I agree with Dr. Parkes that there seems to be an average of two anovulatory cycles following the period of amenorrhea but this again varies greatly. There is no available evidence that would permit us to say whether there is any variation in the number of such cycles in relation to duration of preceding amenorrhea. Nor do I know of any published data that would throw light on the question of whether the chance of conception is reduced by continued lactation after the reappearance of menstruation. I wonder whether Dr. Wyon, who has collected such data in India, can tell us about it.

DR. WYON: As Dr. Tietze said, we are in the first stage of analyzing the data which we collected in the study from the northern Punjab, India, for about five years. We were able to visit women regularly each month and asked them whether they were menstruating, whether or not the previous child survived, and whether they were pregnant. So far the answer is certain among these particular people that lactation tends to be longer than amenorrhea. The probability of conception is much less during amenorrhea than after menstruation has started. According to analyses that have been made thus far it does look as if the number of menstruating months that occurs after the start of menses is of the order of about five to six months. We cannot answer the question about the pituitary because we do not have the data. We are studying the difference in probability of conception among women who are menstruating, comparing those who are lactating with those who are not lactating.

DR. PINCUS: I would like to continue with one aspect of this. It seems to me that either Dr. Greep or Dr. Astwood or their colleagues showed a number of years ago that the very act of suckling insured a period of sterility by an effect on ovulation and the maintenance of pseudo-pregnancy. Has my memory gone bad on me?

DR. GREEP: Yes, I think you have the wrong people.

DR. HISAW: I think this matter Dr. Pincus refers to is of much older vintage than Greep and Astwood. Something like over 30 years ago it was found that after rats gave birth estrous cycles stopped while the young were suckling. Then if a full new litter was put on when the first litter began to quit suckling the estrous cycle could be postponed for at least 21 days, and during this time there was luteal function and lactation. Dr. Sam Leonard was the man who showed this. He found that even on the 21st day he could get decidual reactions. Just how long he carried it on I don't know but he could postpone estrus for a long time.

DR. HERTIG: I'd like to ask Dr. Parkes what the evidence is for these two anovulatory cycles? Is it morphological by examination of the ovaries, endometrium or other tissues during lactation?

DR. PARKES: Yes, as I remember, the gynecologist who talked to me about this had made endometrial biopsies. That's my recollection. I might touch back on this cyclic activity and lactation again. In case of the rat, the facts are perfectly well known, I think, and are rather interesting. If three or more young are being suckled there is no postpartum estrus and no further return of estrus for about three weeks. If only one or two are being suckled then the cycle recurs mainly during lactation. If a second and younger litter is passed on to the mother when the first litter has to be removed then according to my recollection there is no further suppression of the estrous cycle. But a rat has been kept in continuous lactation for a year by continuous foster mothering on new litters and the cycle continues after the initial gap under those circumstances.

DR. WYON: One point has not come out in the discussion so far. Analyses of data from the study of women in the Punjab indicates that length of postpartum amenorrhea varies markedly according to whether or not the child born at the beginning of the interpregnancy interval survived or was an abortion or stillbirth. Delay in onset of menses is the same after children who die in the first month of life as after a stillbirth. Menstruation starts within two months after abortion or miscarriage in 97 per cent of cases and after about five months in 80 per cent of cases following a stillbirth or a neonatal death. But if the child survives a month or more then 50 per cent of the women have no menstruation for 12 months. In almost all these latter cases, lactation continues.

DR. TIETZE: In further answer to Dr. Hertig's question, there are some studies of anovulatory cycles based on endometrial observations and some based on temperature charts.

DR. McARTHUR: Would Professor Parkes be willing to speculate about the possible role of pheromones in human reproduction? Clinicians have tended to attribute "boarding school amenorrhea," for example, to a hypothalamic disturbance reflecting the loneliness of girls away from home for the first time. However, one wonders whether the temporary segregation of a large number of girls in an exclusively female society may not be a contributory factor.

Is it conceivable that pheromones could be deliberately utilized in some manner for purposes of population control?

DR. PARKES: It is easy to speculate in this field, which is all I am asked to do, I think. One aspect of the social odor story which I didn't get around to mentioning is a further manifestation of the mouse story, because as I indicated the appearance of males among uncrowded females will break up the anestrus which has set in and will cause the restart of the cycle with appearance of estrus. Exactly the same thing happens when alien males of a different strain are loosed among newly mated females. Something like 80 per cent of the females under those conditions do not get pregnant and return to estrus within four, five or six days, as though the original mating had never taken place. And that again has been shown quite conclusively, I think, to be due to the smell of the alien males of a different strain which had been put in contact with the newly mated females. By very recent results it looks as though the source of the operative smell of these alien males is their urine which is of some considerable interest because in the human subject odorous steroids are known to be excreted in small quantities. I'm thinking particularly of the $\triangle^{16}$ -androstenol which is a very fine musky smelling steroid and is secreted in perceptible amounts by humans.

DR. ENGEL: I think it is interesting that even androsterone which is a biologically active androgen has a distinctive smell if you warm it up. I think the odor is intrinsic in this compound. Another point is that the ability of humans to smell the $\triangle^{16}$ compound is genetically determined. We passed around samples of these $\triangle^{16}$ compounds in the laboratory and some of us could smell it and some of us couldn't. Unfortunately, my assistant whom I asked to weigh out a sample for a colleague who couldn't smell it, *could* and she has never forgiven me for that.

DR. HOAGLAND: Is there any sex difference according to odor?

DR. ENGEL: Not that I know of.

DR. PARKES: May I ask, Mr. Chairman, you said this was a genetic matter — Did you in fact try to breed from those who couldn't smell it?

DR. ENGEL: I think someone at Harvard in the Department of Social Relations is studying families for ability and inability to smell.

DR. LEVIN: I would like to ask Dr. Parkes about the interesting birth rate data he showed for the various seasons of the year. It seemed that he was almost correlating high conception rates with periods of relaxation at Christmas and also during the summer months. First, I would like to ask if this data is similar to that found in other countries that are comparable to Britain. Secondly, whether with regard to these data he attaches significance to seasonal factors such as variation in the amount of light, in temperature or in other factors of this sort which have been shown to have an effect on reproductive activity of lower animals. Thirdly, I wonder if one can extrapolate from this data in relation to population growth in either of two interesting fashions: as we predict these periods of relaxation and as we become more tense as Dr. Hoagland suggested previously. Perhaps this increase in tension will result in an artificial biological way of reducing conception and therefore births. On the other hand, as we become automated and have more leisure time and, perhaps, become more relaxed, we may get ever greater conception rates and so become more and more overpopulated. I think this is very interesting. I would particularly like to know if the data is common to other countries?

DR. PARKES: Well, I simply don't know precisely. I doubt that very interesting diagram after our Registrar General's reports and I haven't seen it referred to anywhere else. The Registrar General himself doesn't seem to bother about it. I just don't know what the explanation is. But the suggestion that this coincides with periods of relaxation is a very interesting one. I skipped over one very interesting point. The peak of births in March 1957 was unexpectedly low. This of course is for England and Wales. Chopping down the births in March of '57 corresponded with the relative and unexpectedly low number of conceptions in the summer of 1956, and what happened in the summer of 1956 — the Suez crisis, of course!

DR. VENNING: I would like to ask the assembled experts about one point. Dr. Parkes showed that there is a four-day period when conception takes place in relation to a particular menstrual cycle in the human. On the basis of this and on the basis of the variations of the human menstrual cycle I think one would expect a greater degree of effectiveness from the rhythm method than in fact anybody has ever shown. I would like the experts to say whether or not they think there is any evidence that ovulation in the human female can be brought forward by intercourse.

DR. ENGEL: Does anyone wish to comment to this point? Dr. Tietze?

DR. TIETZE: There is a considerable variation in the day of ovulation, i.e., the length of the secretory phase of the cycle, but it is not as great as the total variation of the menstrual cycle since there is also some variation in the luteal phase. Dr. Robert G. Potter of Princeton (now at Brown) and I have constructed a statistical model of the menstrual pattern which shows very clearly that the effectiveness of the rhythm method, correctly taught, correctly understood, and correctly practiced, varies inversely with the variability of the menstrual cycle and also varies directly with the contribution of the luteal phase to variation of the cycle. While Knaus has always maintained with great vigor through these many years that the effectiveness of the rhythm method depends on a luteal phase of rigidly uniform duration, this view is not correct. I cannot say anything about the question whether ovulation in the human female can be produced by coitus or orgasm. The preponderance of opinion seems to be against this assumption.

DR. ENGEL: Thank you, Dr. Tietze. I think the vigor of this discussion is ample testimony to the interest that has been aroused by Professor Parkes' discourse and again we wish to thank him.

CLINICAL STUDIES ON
HUMAN FERTILITY CONTROL

CELSO-RAMON GARCIA

Senior Scientist, Worcester Foundation for Experimental Biology; Chief, Infertility Clinic, Massachusetts General Hospital.

I SHALL ADDRESS my remarks to the biological control of conception and, as my title infers, mainly to those applications in the human of the more successful animal experiments where conception has been controlled through physiological means. By this I mean to exclude the various mechanical devices which had been utilized for control of conception. At the start, I have some question as to how to classify the recently reactivated intrauterine coil; although it is a mechanical device, its mechanism of action still is not clear. Whether this device acts through a local effect or an indirect physiological effect is still an unanswered question, but it is such an effective method that I felt compelled to mention it.

By biological means one might alter fertility by inhibiting implantation, by blocking fertilization, or by controlling the formation or the release of the germ cells in either sex. Within these three major groupings one can classify the various physiological methods by which the fertility of the individual may be controlled.

The prevention of implantation presents more than the usual interest since it implies postcoital control. However, while there have been many laboratory approaches, these either have not been applied to the human or have proved not to be applicable to the human. Although some of the animal experiments suggest great effectiveness, as for example, the folic acid antagonist, in the human they are not only inconsistent but also are rather toxic. Because of this they have not been applied in any widespread studies.

The use of certain compounds, the so-called neutral steroids, has been reported by Banick and Pincus, as well as Hurteau and others, to exhibit a reduction in the numbers of implantations as well as resorption of some of the fetuses. And as the dosage is increased, the effectiveness of preventing implantation likewise is enhanced. Shelesnyak's histamine inhibitors have raised considerable interest but to date, to the best of my knowledge, have not been applied to the human successfully. Segal and Nelson have interfered with ovum development after fertilization with the use of certain compounds labeled as the MER-25 and MRL-41. However, again I must repeat that, to date, no safe and effective means of this type are available for human use.

If we focus our attention to the second major grouping, the prevention of fertilization, the most obvious and, if adhered to, still somewhat successful method is the separation of the males and the females. A periodic abstinence has been used for many years and the studies of this method indicate that the intellect is not fully capable either of coordinating the control of the desire to remain sexually continent or in selecting the proper occasion which would permit avoiding the ovulation phase. So variable are these that the pregnancy rate is still between ten and thirty pregnancies per 100 woman-years even in the highly motivated subjects. I think that Dr. Tietze is better versed in these figures than I am and will comment on them further. Perhaps if impending ovulation might be detectable through simple means, and the subjects were of superior motivation, the application of this so-called "rhythm method" might be more effective.

Another proposed application in prevention of fertilization is to interfere with gamete transport or interfere with the gamete itself. This might be achieved by interfering with the metabolism during transport. If one focuses attention to the lower end of the reproductive tract, a barrier might be achieved through changes in cervical mucus rendering it impenetrable by the spermatozoa. Those of us who were present at the meeting of the International Fertility Association in Brussels heard Juan Zarnatu of Santiago, Chile, present his observations in the detailed study of a group of women who were administered progestins. He pointed out the marked effect that these substances had on the cervical mucus which tended to prevent the penetration of this cervical mucus by the spermatozoa. Unfortunately, on some occasions despite the ingestion of these progestins the numbers of spermatozoa that swim about freely even after many days of progestin therapy may be quite sizeable. Thus, this by itself cannot be relied on completely for conception control.

Perhaps application of some of the observations of Noyes with the administration of various endocrines to the rabbit, producing a diminution in the transport of the spermatozoa, might be applicable to humans. To date this has not been done and the results shown by Noyes are still preliminary.

One might inactivate the gamete within the oviduct. Certain substances such as compound MER-25 have been used under the premise that it might be secreted in the oviduct and produce toxic effects which would interfere with the possible fertilizing potential of the respective gamete. Enzymatic alterations, immunological effects, and the like are still great ponderables. These likewise have not been applied sucessfully to the human.

The control of gametogenesis is the area where some positive applicable steps have been taken toward control of conception by biological means. In males, the use of the progestin-estrogen combinations, as well as androgens, have been utilized in some trials by Heller, Nelson and others. With the progestin and estrogen combinations, while reducing spermatogenesis to significant levels, the undesirable, somewhat destructive effects on the tubules rendered this particular method of little value. Furthermore, the reduction of libido, likewise, was a great disadvantage. The bis compounds, the dichloroacetyl-diamines, which Heller, Nelson, McCloud and others utilized in the human, proved to be quite an effective group of compounds that would reduce spermatogenesis to adequate levels. Although these effects were readily reversible, without effect on the libido, the side effects and potential toxicity under certain conditions did not warrant wider field trials. Again the application of immunology crops up in this area, and Professor Parkes has touched upon this previously.

The first truly practical break-through in the application of physiologic means has been carried out in women. The wilful inhibition of ovulation in the female has long been known. This is not a recent observation. However, the successful application of such suppression through the use of a progestin-estrogen combination has been carried out through the efforts of Gregory Pincus and John Rock and many co-workers. This is by no means a perfect method and no one claims that it is the final answer. We hope that it will serve as a stimulus as to what can be done through the cooperative research endeavors of the basic scientists and the clinicians. Many compounds other than the original progestin-estrogen combinations have now been placed at the disposal of many workers in large field trials throughout the world. I shall attempt to recount some of our experiences with these ovulation inhibitors and shall dwell largely with one of these substances, namely the norethynodrel-mestranol combination which is the one with which we have had the greatest experience.

TABLE 1

Ovulation Inhibitory Activity of Various Classes of Steroids

Type of Compound	# Tested	# Active	% Active
Estrogens & Derivatives	43	9	21
Androgens & Derivatives	35	7	20
Progesterone derivatives	57	15	26
17-OH-progesterone derivatives	19	10	52
19 Nor-steroids	33	23	70

Very early Gregory Pincus and his collaborators at the Worcester Foundation surveyed a great many compounds. In Table 1 these are grouped together according to their predominant endocrine activity as estrogens, androgens and progestins. Estrogens and androgens have long been utilized for suppression of ovulation, as for example in the treatment of dysmenorrhea, but no attempt to do this in a cyclic fashion for any prolonged period of time had been attempted. The estrogens and androgens have certain disadvantages from a practical standpoint; the androgens because of their masculinizing characteristics and the estrogens because of their potential interference and loss of control of the menstrual regularity of the female. And also because of the aura of uneasiness that many individuals have towards the continued unopposed use of estrogens in the female. One can see from this group that amongst the progesterone derivatives there are two groups, the 17-hydroxy-progesterone derivatives and the 19-nor-steroids which showed a much higher percentage of active ovulation inhibitors than that exhibited by progesterone itself. The 19-nor-steroids were the ones that exhibited this effect most dramatically. As a result, it was this particular group that received the greatest concentrated efforts.

In an attempt to select the compound that would be most applicable to our field trials the three compounds that seemed to have the greatest ovulation inhibiting effect in animals were

TABLE 2

Biological Activities in Test Animals of Three 19 Nor-Steroids
Percentage of Standard

19 Nor-Steroid	Andro-genic (a)	Estro-genic (b)	Anti-Estro-genic- (c)	Oral Progesta-tional (d)	Oral Ovula-tion Inhibit-ing (e)
Norethandrolone Nilevar (Searle)	6	0	7000	320	25
Norethindrone Norlutin (Parke-Davis)	3	0	7000	100	160
Norethynodrel (Major ingredient of Enovid) (Searle)	0	3	0	30	200

a) In castrated rat with testosterone proprionate as standard.
b) In ovariectomized rat with some estrone as standard.
c) In immature, estrone-treated mice with testosterone proprionate as standard.
d) In estrogen-primed, immature rabbits with 17 D-acetoxyprogesterone as standard.
e) In immature rabbits with 6α-methyl-17-acetoxyprogesterone as standard.

likewise assayed for relative comparative endocrine potencies in animals (Table 2). The androgenicity was adjudged by the increase in the levator ani weights in castrated rats. The estrogenic effect was assessed by an increase in uterine weights as compared with estrone treated ovariectomized rats. The anti-estrogenic effect was correlated with the effect of administration of testosterone and its effect on inhibiting the increase of uterine weight when the immature mouse is treated with estrone. The histological effects were assayed with the aid of estrogen-primed immature rabbits and the degree of endometrial changes produced compared with the effect obtained with the use of 17-

hydroxy-progesterone as a standard. The oral ovulation inhibiting effect in the mature rabbit was evaluated by palpating the ovary and comparing it with the effect one obtained with a very potent progestin (at least in the rabbit), namely, 6-alpha-methyl-17-hydroxy-progesterone. We can see from the results that the compound, the norethynodrel-mestranol combination (Enovid, Searle), was the one that showed no androgenic effect and was not the least bit antiestrogenic; if anything it showed a slightly estrogenic effect. However, although the oral progestational effect was not as great, the oral ovulation inhibiting effect was greater than the other compounds. For these reasons Enovid (Searle) was selected for our field trials. It more closely resembled the usual hormonal milieu in the female and was a very effective ovulation inhibitor. We realized, and when I say we, I am using an editorial we, because it was Gregory Pincus who so emphasized, that it would be essential to evaluate this compound on the basis of the promise that it had and to do so in large scales so that the over all long-term effects might be assessed. It is as a result of this that we have been enabled to obtain much of our information.

In the initial studies with Compound I, the nor-ethindrone compound (Norlutin, Parke-Davis) and Compound II, the nor-ethynodrel-mestranol combination (Enovid, Searle), it was soon obvious that the menstrual cycle of the human female could be mimicked by administering Compound I in dosages of from 10 to 40 milligrams a day and Compound II in dosages of from 10 to 20 milligrams a day starting on the 5th day of a cycle through the 25th day (Table 3). The mean cycle length closely resembled that of the control group and was what one would expect of the average regularly ovulating female. We assessed the effects exhibited through basal temperature graphs, endometrial biopsies, vaginal smears, pregnanediol and 17-ketosteroid urinary excretion. While the first three of these indirect indices of ovulation might indicate an effect of the medication

TABLE 3

Effects of 17α-Ethynyl-19-Nor-estosterone (I), and 17α-Ethynyl-5(10) Estraeneolone (II) Upon Cycle Length, Indices of Ovulation and Steroid Output in Normal Ovulating Women

Compound	# of cycles	Mean Cycle Length (Days)	Basal Temperature (%−)	Endometrial Biopsy (%−)	Vaginal Smear (%−)	Pregnanediol mg/da	17-Keto-Steroids mg/da
Control	40	27.2 ±0.51	6	0	0	3.4 ±0.27	5.2 ±0.47
I	62	28.5 ±0.68	92	76	81	0.34 ±0.066	4.80 ±0.40
II	34	26.7 ±0.48	82	93	72	0.30 ±0.074	4.5 ±0.47

alone, certainly the marked reduction in pregnanediol excretion was very highly suggestive of ovulation inhibition. In fact, laparotomies subsequently proved this to be the case. Moreover, subsequent studies on the metabolic effects of these substances showed no adverse effects on the various body systems that one could measure, even after long term use. The various blood counts, blood studies, urine analyses, liver function tests, etc., did not show variations to support abnormal metabolic deviations clinically.

The hemostatic effect and the control of the menstrual cycle length by these substances have been very consistent observations amongst all investigators. Figure 1 compares data of normal, regularly ovulating women, taken from data obtained by Haman with similar data of the Enovid treated women in Puerto Rico. The bell-shaped curves show a higher peak around days 26–28 for the women treated with Enovid than for the tracing representing Haman's normal menstrual cycle data. These Puerto

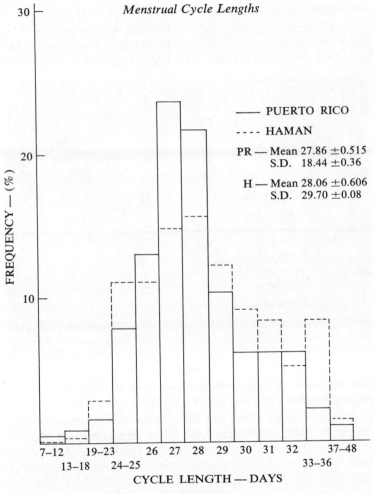

Menstrual Cycle Lengths

——— PUERTO RICO

- - - - HAMAN

PR — Mean 27.86 ±0.515
S.D.   18.44 ±0.36

H — Mean 28.06 ±0.606
S.D.   29.70 ±0.08

FIGURE 1

Rican women were treated with the norethynodrel-mestranol combination from the 5th day to the 24th day inclusive.

Previously I mentioned that laparotomy confirmed that ovulation was suppressed. The appearance of these ovaries are especially dramatic (Figure 2). The outline of a #10 Bard

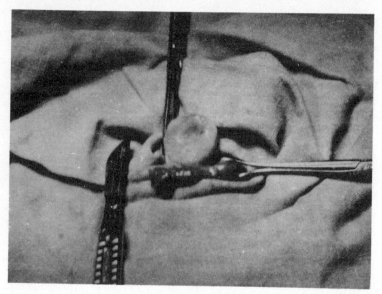

FIGURE 2

CASE R-93 (S.O.) Laparotomy view of ovary Day 29 of 64th cycle. Patient on 5 mg. per day of Enovid.

Parker blade on a #3 scalpel handle serves to give an idea of the size of the ovary. Even after one cycle of therapy, they show a very marked effect from this medication. The gross appearance of the ovary is that of a very inactive or atrophic and menopausal looking ovary. At first glance this might lead one to have some concern were it not for the fact that as is seen in Figure 3 this is quite reversible. Incidentally, the ovary

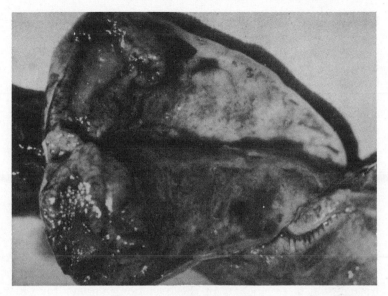

FIGURE 3

CASE R-29 (D.R.) Section of ovary. Cyclic Enovid administration for 5 years until suspension of medication 5½ weeks prior to surgery.

in Figure 2 was from a patient who had been on 64 cycles of medication at the 5 milligram dosage and this laparotomy was performed on day 29 of a treated cycle. She showed a marked ovarian atrophy. The ovary shown in Figure 3 comes from a young lady who has been on cyclic Enovid for a little longer period of time and had a cervical carcinoma in situ. When this was detected, the medication was discontinued and about 5½ to 6 weeks later she had a hysterectomy performed. This is a section through the ovary from the hysterectomy specimen. The large corpus luteum present within the confines of so perfectly normal an ovary is most reassuring of the prompt return of ovarian function. This is what we have observed in the patients who have been on medication for varying periods of time, many for some six or seven years. Now, we have seen the gross effects on the ovaries. The microscopic findings have been reported previously by our group indicating that at least in the preliminary comparison of treated patients compared to normal women there wasn't any significant variation in the oocyte population density. Since then, we have had many more sections of even longer term therapy and the preliminary counts likewise tend to indicate the same status. Furthermore, some question has been raised concerning the possible differences that might be detected in the differential follicle counts to indicate a possibility of a greater degree of damage to the ovary, through atresia. This might be noted by an increase in the atretic follicle population. Again our preliminary differential counts do not seem to substantiate this.

Table 4 shows the effects on the return of ovulation in women treated with large amounts of the ovulation inhibitor for prolonged intervals. These 20 women were treated for endometriosis in an ascending scale of medication to suppress menstruation,

TABLE 4

Effect on Recurrence of Ovulation Following
Cessation of Long-Term Enovid* Therapy
for Endometriosis

No. of patients followed up	Postmedication cycle (No.)	Mean cycle length (days)	% Ovulating
13	First	36	70
7	Second	27	100

* The regimen was as follows: 10 mg/day for 2 weeks; 20 mg/day for the 3rd and 4th week; then 30 mg/day for 2 to 3 months.

in hopes that the endometriosis would be regressed or destroyed. All of these women had urinary gonadotropins determinations obtained periodically before going on treatment, during treatment and after coming off treatment. They all eventually failed to have detectable levels of gonadotropin excretion. However, after cessation of medication they all had a return of detectable levels of gonadotropin secretion. By the second post-medication cycle, even after such massive therapy, all had resumed ovulation. Similar observations have been noted with doses as high as 100 milligrams a day, given daily, for as long as a year's time.

TABLE 5

Pregnancies According to Pills Missed (San Juan)

Number of pills missed	Dose (mg/day)	Number of women years	Number of pregnancies	Pregnancy rate per 100 women years
	2.5	411	1*	0.2
0	5.0	1685	4	0.2
	10.0	686	4	0.6
	2.5	77	0	0.0
1–5	5.0	154	4	2.6
	10.0	95	3	3.2
	2.5	6	4	66.7
6–19	5.0	19	8	42.1
	10.0	31	10	32.3

* Patient took ½ tablet (1.25 mg/day)

The efficacy of this therapy has long since been shown to be quite reliable except when the patient misses medication (Table 5). The more tablets missed, the greater is the likelihood of pregnancy. This is borne out by the higher incidence of pregnancy by those skipping tablets. Of interest also from these data is the fact that some patients apparently do establish pregnancies during cycles of administration. While one does raise the question, after inspecting the ovaries at the many laparotomies, as to whether we are obtaining the correct information from these women, the fact that they insist that they are speaking the truth has to be considered. This is weighted further by the fact that with the norethindrone-mestranol combination (Orthonovum, Ortho), Goldzieher has measured progestational levels of pregnanediol in isolated cycles. He assumes that this is an escape ovulation and that the pregnancy is made less likely because of the cervical mucus changes blocking spermatozoa. If so, this escape ovulation occurs with great infrequency. In any event, if it does occur and pregnancy follows in those cycles where medication is taken, even if erratically, certainly the effect of these substances on the endometrium does not inhibit or interfere with implantation. Also, it would appear likely that, at least with this norethynodrel-mestranol medicated group, there don't seem to be any deleterious effects on the offspring because all of these infants born during the medicated cycles were quite normal at birth.

TABLE 6

	Number of subjects	Pregnancies per 100 years of exposure
Before Use	838	117
During Use	838	1
After Withdrawal	239	233
Those Withdrawing After 1 to 4 Years Of Use	101	277

Adeline Pendleton in Humacao tabulated the fertility, as indicated by pregnancies per 100 years of exposure before use, during use, after withdrawal, and after 1 to 4 years of use (Table 6). The marked reduction in fertility which occurs in those individuals taking these ovulation inhibitors and the somewhat increased pregnancy rate which is seen after stopping this method is evident. Of course, this is somewhat weighted by the promptness with which many of these pregnancies occurred. It is of interest to note also that in this group about 50 per cent of the pregnancies occurred within the first two cycles after cessation. Goldzieher, in a smaller group of women who had used the norethindrone-mestranol combination, found that about 60 per cent of these women established a pregnancy within the first cycle after cessation of therapy which is more than one should expect by mere probability and in any one cycle.

TABLE 7

COMPARATIVE STUDY

Various Symptoms — % Complaining

Symptoms	Enovid	Orthonovum	Ovulin
Gastro-intestinal	13	10	10
Subjective	20	19	14
Vaginal & Lower Abdominal Distress	6	7	6
Breakthrough Bleeding	6	1	2
All Symptoms	28	32	28

Table 7 is again some of Adeline Pendleton's data comparing the various symptoms among the users of Enovid, Orthonovum and Ovulin. All were used at approximately the two milligram dosage level per day. The most common complaints which the patients have are gastro-intestinal, lower abdominal pain, breakthrough bleeding, various minor subjective symptoms, and weight gain. The observations are fairly similar with all three compounds. Perhaps Orthonovum may exhibit a little less breakthrough bleeding but at the same time, Orthonovum does predispose slightly to weight gain. This is not shown in this tabulation. The aspect of weight gain has been observed not only by Adeline Pendleton and the group in Puerto Rico, but also by Edris Rice-Wray in Mexico City.

The potential deleterious suppressive effect of these compounds on the adrenals has been raised. Although there is a marked reduction in pregnandiol late in the cycle in comparison with an untreated cycle, this is subsequent to ovarian inhibition.

TABLE 8
Urinary Steroid Excretion (mg/24 hrs.)
Mean Values

| | | 11-OH Corticoids | | 17-KS | |
		Enovid	Control	Enovid	Control
During Enovid Rx	Pre Rx	8.90 ±4.34	—	9.28 ±2.99	—
	Pre ACTH	3.54 ±1.88	7.08 ±1.36	4.90 ±2.74	7.25 ±2.32
	Day 1 ACTH 80 u im	19.01 ±9.14	21.33 ±6.52	12.12 ±6.19	16.52 ±8.07
	Day 2 ACTH 80 u im	22.94 ±8.62	22.82 ±12.05	17.09 ±1.85	22.74 ±15.68

TABLE 9
Urinary Steroid Excretion (mg/24 hrs.)
Mean Values

| | | Pregnantriol | | Pregnanediol | |
		Enovid	Control	Enovid	Control
During Enovid Rx	Pre Rx	—	—	—	—
	Pre ACTH	0.64 ±0.38	1.74 ±0.72	0.73 ±0.34	1.42 ±0.76
	Day 1 ACTH 80 u im	2.48 ±1.13	5.34 ±2.32	0.94 ±0.03	1.90 ±0.50
	Day 2 ACTH 80 u im	4.96 ±4.31	9.95 ±7.47	1.44 ±1.11	3.40 ±2.89

The reductions in 17-keto steroids and hydroxy corticoids are of a much smaller magnitude. That this does not affect the responsiveness of the adrenal to ACTH stimulation is shown in the data gathered by Edward Wallach (Table 8). The functional capacity of this gland can be assessed by the increase in preg-

TABLE 10
Plasma. Total Cortisol. Mean value mg/100 ml

	Enovid	Control
Prior to ACTH	23.45 4.78 S.E. 2.76	10.90 3.21 S.E. 1.85
Day I–ACTH 80 u im	44.35 11.22 S.E. 6.48	18.32 4.58 S.E. 2.64
Day II–ACTH 80 u im	39.71 10.1 S.E. 5.78	12.14 3.46 S.E. 1.99

TABLE 11
Effects of Enovid on Lactating Women (Humacao)

Dosage mg/day	Total # Followed Up	% Lactating Less than Previously	% Lactating Same as Previously	% Lactating More than Previously
20	22	77	18	5
18	37	38	57	5
5	84	45	45	10
2.5	34	15	70	15

nanediol and pregnantriol levels following ACTH administration (Table 9). More convincing, in Table 8, we see that there is a similar rise in the 17-ketosteroids and the hydroxy corticoids after this adrenal stimulation. In Table 10 there is some indication that the plasma cortisols are somewhat elevated and this may explain the compensatory reduction in the urinary corticoids. After ACTH, the plasma cortisols likewise show an elevation.

Of interest is the question which has been raised concerning the possible suppressive effects on lactation. We don't know the answer. There are some data indicating suppression of lactation if therapy at 10–20 mg/day is initiated immediately postpartum. However, in the usual ovulation suppressive doses initiated 6–8 weeks postnatally, no complaints of suppression have been elicited in a rather small sampling. In Table 11, showing some of

Adeline Pendleton's data, where the medication is started early in the third postpartum week, we see that at the higher dosage level, there may be somewhat of a reduction in lactation. Now lactation is indeed very complex. How to control and assess the various factors is indeed difficult to answer. At least in questioning those multiparous women whom Dr. Pendleton followed, there was very little complaint of lactation suppression at the lower dosage schedule.

Much has been said regarding the administration of these substances and the occurrence of thrombophlebitis. Despite vast efforts which have been expended in regard to epidemiological surveys as well as on various coagulation studies, no satisfactory answer has been arrived at to date. No causal effect relationship has been established but neither has it been established that there is none. While there have been individual blood coagulation factor variations, their role in this problem is unknown. When asked the specific question: does this promote or aid in increasing the incidence of thrombophlebitis?, the answer has been consistently, we do not know. There aren't any clinical indications that they play a role. In many instances, the increase in a specific individual factor, e.g., factor VII, has been shown not to influence blood coagulation. Moreover, while the statistics that are available are not truly comparable, certainly they are not indicative of an increased incidence of thrombophlebitis. Everyone is "grasping for straws" to shed light on this vexing question. In the Puerto Rican and Haitian studies, we examined these patients for the presence of varicosities and much to our surprise after Gregory Pincus assembled this data, seen in Table 12, the control group had a significantly higher incidence of varices than the treated group. Now varicosities are felt by some to predispose to thrombophlebitis. When this aspect was pursued further, the statistically significant lowering of incidence was found in the group that had been on medication for the longest period of time. In a rather simple way, one might explain this by the fact that these patients were further removed from pregnancy than their control sisters. Therefore the congestive effects of pregnancy on these vessels was not as troublesome as in the unmedicated group.

TABLE 12

Data on Varicosities — Enovid Users and Controls Examined in Puerto Rico and Haiti — December 1962

Dose of Enovid	Number of patients	% with varices
None (Controls)	63	49.2 ± 5.3
2.5 mg	58	29.5 ± 6.0
5.0 mg.	106	28.3 ± 4.5

Years of Use	Number of patients	% with varices
Controls	63	49.2 ± 6.2
0–2	23	26.1 ± 9.2
2–4	79	31.7 ± 5.2
4–6	62	25.8 ± 5.5

[*Question by Dr. Rock:* Was there an attempt made to correlate the controls with age and parity of the treated patients?]

Age and parity were correlated and there wasn't any particular significant difference in the two groups.

Another aspect where there has been some concern has been the carcinogenic potential of these substances. Table 13 is an old one. I do not have the more recent data for presentation. However, it shows a similar pattern. There have been some class IV and V smears but still at a much lower incidence than, for example, in the Lyndon Lee series. Lee surveyed a segment of the Puerto Rican population and found a moderately high incidence of carcinoma of the cervix in his sampling. If our survey of women on Enovid followed his sampling, we should have had a higher incidence of abnormal smears. However, this was not the case and follow-up likewise has substantiated this. We are presently in the throes of a random sampling-blind distribution with a control group and an oral contraceptive treated group. We hope this will permit a more sound evaluation of the effect of Enovid on the incidence of the attack rate of cancer of the genital system. The data to date merely permit one to say that it doesn't seem to have a carcinogenic effect.

TABLE 13

Vaginal Cytology in Medicated Subjects
Compared with that Found for Puerto Rican Women Generally

Smear Type		Incidence in this series % 412 smears	Incidence in series of Lee et al. % 11,664 smears
I	Normal	85	62
II	Atypical benign	15	33
III	Suspicious	0.2	3.3
IV	Ca-in-Situ	0.0	0.5
V	Malignant cancer	0.0	0.6

In Table 14 one can compare the relative effectiveness of the various methods of conception control. Enovid represents the oral contraceptive. Let us compare the various average pregnancy rates expressed as pregnancies per 100 woman-years of exposure with the various methods of conception control. We can see that using douches it is 31, the safe period 24, jelly alone 20, withdrawal 18, condom 14, diaphragm with or without jelly 12, and the oral contraceptive 1.2.

[*Question by Dr. Hoagland:* What's the pregnancy rate with no contraceptives for those data?]

It varies somewhat; for Puerto Rico the figure given for the pregnancy rate in women not using contraceptives is 60 to 100 pregnancies per 100 woman-years. I think Dr. Tietze would be able to answer that for us more accurately.

[*Dr. Tietze:* In the proper comparison for this set of figures, it would be in the vicinity of 150 to 200 because these are all equal, observed with comparison of a short period. Therefore long exposures as well as the postpartum amenorrhea effect which influences the figure of 60 to 100 does not come into play with proper comparison, but I would say 150 to 200.]

TABLE 14
Effectiveness of Different Methods
of Conception Control

Method	Average pregnancy rate per 100 woman-years
Douche	31
Safe Period	24
Jelly alone	20
Withdrawal	18
Condom	14
Diaphragm (with or without jelly)	12
Enovid	1.2*

*Average pregnancy rate on 578 woman-years (c. 7000 cycles) including cycles in which tablets have been missed.

Again I wish to indicate that we are really in the very early phases of the application of physiologic data to fertility regulation. Many animal studies require application to the human. Again I would like to enter the plea, a very strong plea, to have more of the basic science people become interested in this problem and to work in closer cooperation with the clinician, and for the clinician to work in closer cooperation with the basic scientist.

DISCUSSION

Dr. Engel declared the meeting open for discussion.

JOHN MACISCO: This is largely a question in regard to experimental design. I was wondering, with respect to the table for pregnancies according to pills missed, what the data would have looked like if controlled by frequency of coitus and age.

DR. GARCIA: All the women in the field trials fall within the reproductive age group and are under age 40. They have proven fertility and their stated coital frequency is continuously recorded. No statistically significant difference has been elicited when comparing the stated coital activity before and during medicated cycles. If anything, in the Haitian trials, there is a suggestion that there might be a slight increase in the coital frequency during the medically protected cycles.

Might I digress for a moment to make a comment concerning a point that was discussed earlier concerning method of administration of the medication. Reference was made to John Cobb of Lahore, West Pakistan, who administered medication according to the lunar cycle. I should like to refer to Charles Flowers of Chapel Hill, N.C., who has been carrying on a study for a little less than a year in which he likewise is dealing with a population that normally does not know how to count. He wished to determine whether it might be feasible to dispense with the close supervision. Usually such organizational provision is necessary with these patients to insure that they take the tablets according to the cyclic schedule. Accordingly, he gave these patients the medication and simply asked them to take a tablet daily ad infinitum or until they had a menstrual flow. Apparently, to date, he has not observed any adverse effects and no pregnancies have occurred.

EDWARD LAUMANN: I wonder if you could expand a little on the symptoms table, particularly the subjective. I was wondering how you characterized or identified subjective symptoms. Also, among the control people who were to be given the placebos, might this percentage of symptoms perhaps be expected to occur in people who were just concerned about doing something to their systems? I wonder if you could expand on this.

DR. GARCIA: Yes, a small placebo sub-study has been carried out in Puerto Rico. Symptoms of headaches, nausea, vomiting, vague aches and pains as well as other miscellaneous complaints were reported, not only in the treated group, but also in the placebo group. The incidence of these complaints was slightly higher, of course, in the treated group. Not only subjective but some objective complaints were also elicited. Somewhat surprising was the slightly higher incidence of breakthrough bleeding in the placebo group among the individuals who were forewarned that they might have some reactions. The effect, be it possible through the hypothalamus, was quite striking. There is no question that some of these complaints were undoubtedly brought on, as we see with any form of medication that is given to a patient. A certain amount of apprehension is responsible, but nonetheless there was a significantly higher incidence of side effects in the treated group versus the placebo group.

MR. LAUMANN: I just want to pursue one more aspect of the subjective symptoms. In the interview with these people, did you try to find out whether, when they declined to continue taking this drug, this was related to their reporting of these kinds of subjective symptoms?

DR. GARCIA: I don't have any tabulations of this but we have some suggestive evidence that if the patients take the medication at night on a full stomach, there seems to be a little lower incidence of the complaints. And another aspect which I did not mention is that the longer the subjects are on medication, the lower the incidence of the side effects. A much higher incidence of complaints is recorded during the early cycles of taking the medication.

DR. HISAW: Our discussion is going to take an interesting turn. We have a great number of young men and women here who should be heard. Dr. García's lecture has raised many, many questions in my mind. That is, one or two people like myself could take up all of our discussion.

There is, however, one thing of a general nature that should be mentioned. Dr. García expressed the hope at the end of his talk that more people get interested in the basic science of these problems. I would like to call your attention to the fact that in times gone by there was in this country what one might call a sort of "monkey fraternity." That is, it was made up of a number of people who worked during those times on several aspects of primate reproduction. There were about seven of them; two of them are now dead, one has gone administrator, three are inactive, and I'm the only remaining exhibit of the group who yet works with monkeys. I have knowledge of several regional primate laboratories in this country and in each case I have asked earnestly, "What are you doing on primate reproduction?" You may know we have sponsored a number of primate laboratories over the United States by government grants and are spending quite a few millions of dollars. So far, I have failed to find a single instance of active research on primate reproduction. I don't know what is going on in England, Dr. Parkes, but are the old monkey men dying off? Are you getting any new ones?

DR. PARKES: May I say that our oldest monkey man is now doing something else.

DR. B. K. ADADEVOH: Might I ask you to elaborate more on your data with regard to the thrombophlebitis issue since, as you say, this is one of the things to keep in mind. You indicated, if I remember the chart, the percent of varices in the various groups. Do you mean varices prior to the particular drugs or are these the incidence of varices as a correlation on the incidence of thrombophlebitis or what exactly is that? The second point concerns the multiple effect or side effects of all these drugs. I suppose this issue comes up from time to time, certainly the one on the adrenal where you showed evidence which shows the response of the adrenals with these drugs. At the same time there was a slight depression in the function, if I remember correctly. Don't you think that it is too premature to consider that these drugs have at least no adrenal effects and if so do any of these matters bear on the issue?

DR. GARCIA: With regard to the material on the varices, we were really grasping for straws as is everyone else who is trying to come up with an answer as to whether there is or is not a causal effect relationship between the administration of Enovid and the occurrence of thrombophlebitis. I don't think anyone can say that they know that there is or there isn't. Certainly there is nothing that indicates that there is, if the conclusions are to be based on available scientific data. Moreover, even when considering the various coagulating factors, even the coagulation experts do not agree amongst themselves as to what their significance is in thromboembolic phenomena.

If we don't know the significance of these various factors how can we go ahead and apply them to this clinical entity? We first have to learn more about the coagulation mechanisms. Perhaps we shall find that the coagulation mechanisms have nothing to do with thrombophlebitis. The old thought may have been something Virchow gave us years back and a concept merely handed down in the literature with the passing of time. I don't think this is the case but even this possibility has been raised. Certainly a blood clot is different histologically from a thrombus.

Varices have long been associated similarly with thrombophlebitis. We haven't seen any instances of thrombophlebitis in some 3000 women in our trials and at present, in the United States alone, between one and two million women are or have been on this form of fertility control with very few occurrences of thromboembolic phenomena. I think Dr. Tietze can give us the exact figures on that but it is immaterial.

In regard to your comments concerning adrenal function, the administration of these substances does appear to lower corticoid excretion in the urine slightly. Actually these differences are really not statistically significant but they're also correlated with a similar rise in the plasma corticoid levels. The plasma corticoid levels show this increase, which probably accounts for the slight decrease in urinary levels. The long term patients, on relatively massive doses, the endometriosis group, likewise, show a similar effect. Moreover, it is not any more pronounced than the lower dosage, cyclic-administered Enovid produces. The fact that the adrenal responds so well to ACTH stimulation is indicative of the fact that adrenal function is not interfered with by whatever alterations are occurring.

It has long been known, for example, that if you administer estrogens, and even during normal pregnancy, that the protein-bound iodine is elevated and this does not mean that these patients are hyperthyroid nor that thyroid function is altered adversely. Similar effects are seen with these fertility regulators. Indeed, by clinical evaluation, there is no indication that the women on these ovarian inhibitors are hyperthyroid. The fact that there is an estrogen component or estrogen effect with these substances is quite apparent, and we look upon this as an estrogen effect. There is no indication that even with the long term therapy there is any alteration or any change of greater magnitude than those mentioned. Therefore, we feel that there isn't any reason to suspect any harmful long term effects.

DR. PARKES: May I bring up very briefly the question of mode of action of these oral progestagens in suppressing ovulation? I want to bring that up because there has been apprehension about this in England over the last year or two. This arises from studies carried out at the Medical Research Council and the Clinical Endocrinological Laboratory in Edinburgh, where they have been examining the excretion of patterns of gonadotropin, pregnanediol, and the estrogens during cycles which are being regulated and in which ovulation has been suppressed by oral progestagens. What they have found, as you would expect, is that the estrogen peak does not appear and that the pregnanediol peak afterwards is also suppressed. But according to the Edinburgh results, the gonadotropin peak of excretion at the time of ovulation is not effected and from that they deduce rightly or wrongly that the triumvirate effect in suppressing ovulation is not suppression of pituitary gonadotropin. And I think we have all assumed with some good evidence that that was the way these things worked. Now, yet another group of critics in England have picked up this observation and say, "Well, that means that the inhibitory effect is direct on the ovary," and yet another group says, "In that case it is almost certainly acting by damaging the oocyte, probably, with genetic results." There is this very awkward fire being leveled at the technique in England at the present time and if anybody has any information of this, I'd like to take it back with me.

DR. GARCIA: I would like to address a few comments to this effect. I alluded to several of these in my presentation. I believe that the data that has been presented and that is available show that depending on the agent, the dosage and the length of time of administration of these substances, one can get a suppression of gonadotropin excretion. The detection of urinary gonadotropins will go down to zero detectable levels with the norethynodrel-mestranol combination if administered in sufficient doses for a long enough time. Now, I think the data to which you refer are those of Loraine and Brown where they use a different substance than the one used in our study. I believe they used medroxy-progesterone (Provera, Upjohn) and with the dosage schedule used, the gonadotropin excretion is unaffected and suggests therefore that the effect is at the ovarian level. Now, I believe that there is also evidence even with the lower dosage of Enovid (Searle) that the effect is mediated directly at the ovary as well. There is suggestive evidence, in any event, that it is directed at the ovary as well as at the hypophysis. The problem which has resulted is that people have grouped all progestins into one category, and suddenly they feel that they all act exactly the same. It has long been shown that Provera by itself is a very poor ovulation inhibitor in the human. This can be aided with the addition of estrogen. At the conference in Brussels, Stickel indicated that with the use of some of the other progestins, for example, 9-alpha-fluoro-11-hydroxy-16-metholene and 17-acetoxy progesterone, ovulation was inhibited at the low dosage level, and that he had a very slight reduction in pregnanediol; at the higher dosage that ovulation was inhibited and that there was a more marked reduction in pregnanediol. Another worker with another progestin compound, (Linestrol, Organon) reported an increase in pregnanediol. All of which, I think, suggests that there is an alteration in the steroid metabolism going on within the ovary. There is even stronger evidence reported by Diczfalusy with the use of the Provera in larger doses, and the concomitant administration of the human hypophyseal gonadotropin. It was noted that the normal rise in estrogen excretion that he normally found preceding ovulation is suppressed. Moreover, if Medroxyprogesterone (Provera, Upjohn) was not administered, ovarian stimulation was achieved, indicating a blockage point at the ovarian level. Lunenfeld, likewise, presented very similar sort of data so that there is increasing evidence that there probably is a dual effect both at the hypophyseal level as well as at the ovarian level, depending on the progestin and depending on the dosage and the length of administration. The final conclusion as to the exact mechanism is still not answered.

DR. PARKES: Whether the effect is direct on the ovary as with some substances and some doses, the mechanism is not known at all. Is that the sum and substance?

DR. GARCIA: At the present time it is not known.

DR. PARKES: There is evidence that there is an ovarian effect, but how it works is not known.

DR. GARCIA: One doesn't even know what the exact mechanism is whereby the functions in the normal ovary are governed, never mind those which are effected through treatment with an exogenously administered estrogen and progestin. Various indirect studies seem to show certain things that one can measure and certain of these measurable points can be altered with the administration of the exogenous progestins and estrogens.

DR. PARKES: Would you say that the effect is on the oocyte with possible genetic effects? That's the crux of the matter.

DR. GARCIA: Well, let me point out that this is a very unlikely thing for two reasons. First of all, our preliminary differential counts on ovarian tissue from treated and untreated women do not fall in line with those in the animal studies of Anita Mandl and the group at Birmingham. Our counts follow the pattern of what you would expect in the normal untreated ovarian section. Now it is true that we are looking at sections of the ovary and we are not doing follicle counts of the entire ovary. However, the promptness with which pregnancy occurs, the promptness with which ovulation occurs after the cessation of medication, and in some instances apparently during the cycles of administration, together with the normalcy of these infants, likewise tend to indicate that the concern raised in this area is more theoretical than practical.

WILLIAM DYSON: I have two questions for Dr. García. The first goes back to one of the early topics raised in regard to the problem of side effects. The first three of the four items were reported as "objective" effects. These three items were the gastrointestinal side effects, distressful generalized symptoms, and people having psychosomatic complaints, all of which could be also classified as subjective. Then on the breakthrough bleeding you discussed the question of placebos which seemed to indicate also a subjective element. So I would like you to clarify the criteria used for classifying these side effects either as subjective or objective and the implications for the other side effects. My second question deals with a reference you made in your paper and which you dealt with very briefly. You mentioned substances that had an effect on the reduction of libido; I wonder if you might expand on this point too.

DR. GARCIA: In reference to the matter concerning side effects, the way in which our data have been accumulated, I should like to point out that any complaint which the patient mentioned is recorded by either a social worker or a nurse who visits the patient every other month. Moreover, these patients are also seen approximately every nine to twelve months or so and examined and interrogated by the medical and auxiliary staff. Each patient is asked, in addition to what she volunteers, if everything is going well and has she any particular problem. We do not go into any specific detailed questioning regarding nausea, vomiting, etc., to avoid possible suggestive effects. Detailed questioning was carried out with the placebo sub-study but not with the overall group from which was compiled the general listing shown in the slide.

MR. DYSON: Just on that point, what I intended to ask even more sharply is what do you mean by "subjective" and how do you distinguish it from the other "objective" symptoms?

DR. GARCIA: Obviously the gastrointestinal likewise can come under the category of subjective. I was merely listing in a separate category those subjective symptoms or complaints that the patient might have which were referable to the gastrointestinal tract, since they are the most numerous, and lumping together the various other smaller categories into a group called subjective.

MR. DYSON: Sort of a wastebasket category.

DR. GARCIA: That is correct.

DR. RENWICK: May I ask how you controlled the plasma cortisols? Did you take them at certain times throughout the day and do you consider this a reliable test of adrenal function? How did you measure urinary gonadotropin? If you use Klinefelter's method it is less sensitive than that of Loraine which determines total excretory gonadotropin activity in terms of human menstrual gonadotropin.

Lastly, did you study the incidence of breast cancer in the long-term treated patient?

DR. GARCIA: I'll answer your last question first. We have not had any cases of carcinoma of the breast in these patients and we have no other information to suggest such a likelihood. If anything, there is a suggestion on the basis of our physical examination that the longer these patients are on this progestin therapy, the less granular is the feel of the breast to the examiner in the follow-up examinations. What this may mean is a moot point. As far as the gonadotropins — Eugenia Rosenberg was the one who performed these determinations and she used the increase in uterine weight method for detecting the gonadotropin excretion. Now with regard to plasma cortisol, perhaps Gregory Pincus would like to answer this. He wanted to ask a question and perhaps make a comment. May we hear from Dr. Pincus?

DR. PINCUS: First of all I would like to clarify the placebo experiment. We used a double blind experiment. The patients received code-numbered tablets. Neither the social worker handing them out nor the supervising physician knew who was getting what. The incidence of so called side effects, $23\% \pm 4.6$ for the true medication and $17.2\% \pm 5.7$ for the placebo are not significantly different. There is a very large literature on the effects of placebos which I don't need to go into here, but generally the implication is that within any one month a significant percentage (about 10 per cent usually) of patients taking placebos complain of "undesirable" effects.

Now as far as the significance of the plasma cortisol is concerned, these were all taken in the morning under normal conditions, so they represent what we might call the probable diurnal maximum that we ordinarily see in normal circumstances. Therefore the increase in total which you see in Enovid treated patients is unquestionably the increase due to an increased plasma transcortin binding additional cortisol. This is attributable to the estrogen as has been shown by many people. As a matter of fact, Dr. Layne, who is here, has measured this and perhaps Dr. Layne ought to talk to us not only about the increase in plasma transcortin, but, much more important, the true secretion rate in these patients. We have measured this using isotope techniques, and this is the real question, because urine and blood concentrations are merely signs of what is truly going on.

DR. DONALD LAYNE: The level of plasma cortisol is definitely increased in women taking Enovid. This is almost certainly due to increased plasma levels of transcortin which are in turn a reflection of the estrogenic potency of the compound. We have shown in our laboratory that estrogens — and Enovid in sufficient dosage — although they increase the plasma level, actually decrease the secretion rate of cortisol to a small but significant extent. Norethynodrel in the purified form with very little estrogen has a smaller effect on cortisol secretion rate.

DR. HENRY VAILLANT: I should like to ask, Dr. García, whether, given the more or less primitive situation you mentioned in the North Carolina study where women are seen, given the pills, and told to take them on their own, how often in such situations do you think the women should be seen by the physician? I ask this because pills seem such a neat idea for providing contraception in so-called underdeveloped countries but in view of all the questions that have just been raised, it seems important at this stage that these women be seen fairly frequently by physicians. Would you comment on the potential dangers of using this pill in relatively unsupervised clinical populations?

DR. GARCIA: This particular question has been raised repeatedly and the public health service officers have asked this also of Mary Calderone. What sort of physical examination or examinations should be carried out to insure the safety of giving the oral contraceptive? She polled a large number of heads of departments of various medical schools throughout the country and also various individuals who had extensive clinical experience with the progestins. She posed this question and she requested that one omit what one might consider an extension of good medical practice for every female in this age group who is not taking this medication. In other words, what examinations are indicated merely because a woman is taking the oral contraceptive? Since these oral agents are mildly estrogenic and estrogens may have a trophic effect on certain leiomyomas, I believe it was recommended that these patients should be checked at about a month or six weeks after instituting therapy and then probably just once a year thereafter. Thus, the concensus is that an initial examination before going on therapy followed by an examination a month or six weeks later and then once a year thereafter is all that is really required for the safe administration of this medication.

DR. R. A. CHIERI: Is the high incidence of pregnancy when the pill was withdrawn a rebound effect? Or is it due to the fact that women wanted to become pregnant and in that way the pregnancy incidence is going to be higher than in a normal population?

DR. GARCIA: The women in question were all women who wanted a temporary method of conception control. When these women stopped medication they did so because they desired to establish a pregnancy. I wish to emphasize that these were women who wanted to become pregnant and this can be an influencing factor. In spite of this, however, the number of pregnancies established in the first cycle after stopping medication is unusually high. As to what underlying mechanisms are involved, I do not have the slightest inkling. There are those who feel that there are certain changes which are produced in the endometrium which enhance implantation. Dr. Hertig, who was here, might have been able to shed some light on this. My impression has been on the basis of information that we get from those who have worked in this area that the conceptus is really searching for a source of nourishment from the maternal blood sources and not glycogen or any other secretions that come from the glandular elements. If a vascular bed is available, this is where implantation is going to occur. The fact that pregnancies implant in the oviduct, pregnancies implant in the peritoneal cavity and so on are an indication that you don't need all of the glandular niceties that people speak about and which they are trying to improve to correct the so-called inadequate luteal phase.

DR. ENGEL: Thank you very much, Dr. García. I think again that the vigor of the discussion has been an index of our appreciation of Dr. García's paper and I would like to close the meeting by once more thanking him and Professor Parkes for providing us with a most exciting and stimulating session.

III

FIELD STUDIES ON FERTILITY
OF HUMAN POPULATIONS
John B. Wyon, M.B., B.Ch., M.PH.

CHANGING FERTILITY IN TAIWAN
Ronald Freedman, Ph.D.

Chairman: Frederick L. Hisaw, Ph.D.

Dr. Hisaw, *in opening the Session, commented that the survival of a species today, regardless of what species, depends upon two factors: upon nature and upon the whims of man. "We have many examples of the works of nature in such matters, and the fossil remains of numerous species are good testimonies to its effectiveness. Nature's processes are certain, ruthless, unemotional, impartial and as sure as death. We know the way nature solves its problems. The influence of man, or rather the intervention of intellect, is a recent innovation, biologically speaking. On the one hand this influence has led to extinctions of species; on the other, some species have met with man's favor and have prospered (if we can think of domestication as prospering). Still other species have met man's fancy and have been protected in reservations or preserves, and a great number of species have not yet even come to man's attention.*

"The problem that we are discussing will be solved," said Professor Hisaw, "either by man or by nature. Nature has its way of doing things which is not always in keeping with good manners but it is certain. What about man himself? What is he going to do about the age-old problem of overproduction? Nature has a solution, as I have mentioned, and has practiced it. Now the question remains, will man acquiesce to the consequences and certainty of his fate or can he modify it, postpone it, or perhaps avoid it?

"The great development of man's brain endows him with superior intellect and the unique capacity of abstraction. These did not originate for the purpose of thinking but rather as products of the evolutionary requirements for survival. He has used this ability for abstraction to construct for himself an intellectual world apart from the mundane and tinged, to say the least, with self-interest, fantasy, flattery, hopes, and a frequent disregard for factual guidance. For instance, he has been telling himself and his progeny, generation after generation for thousands of years, that he was created as a crowning feature in the image of his maker and to that extent is in special favor with his creator. With such self-flattery and false assurance he goes whistling by the graveyard that contains the fossil remains of his anthropoid ancestors who were weighed in the impartial balance of survival, for some good reason were found wanting, and consequently are now extinct. Modern man seldom reflects on the possibility that he too may be traveling down this same fateful road trod by his ancestors.

"The question that is before us, it seems to me, is that of finding the most promising possibility of a solution. This seems to rest on concrete efforts of three groups of intellectual disciplines: the biological sciences, medicine and the social sciences. The first two must supply the scientific facts and their practical application to the situation, and we have already heard about some of that. The third must find ways of integrating these find-

ings into a workable whole that is acceptable to mankind. This tripod of support, as we might think of it, holds the hopes of our efforts. No one leg is stronger than the other and if one fails, the whole structure will collapse. So, to me at least, it is a very serious business that we have to talk about. It is not about something that is imminent, something that is going to happen tomorrow; it is not as dramatic as the atomic bomb but it is just as capable of destroying mankind."

After these introductory remarks, the Chairman then presented the speakers for the third session, Dr. John B. Wyon and Dr. Ronald Freedman.

FIELD STUDIES ON FERTILITY

OF HUMAN POPULATIONS

JOHN B. WYON

Assistant Professor of Population Studies, Harvard School of Public Health; former field director, India-Harvard Population Study.

I was very glad to hear Dr. Hisaw mention the three legs of the tripod of knowledge that are needed in order to solve population problems. I shall be making use of the concept of ecology and I think perhaps this is what Dr. Hisaw had in mind when he mentioned the three aspects. Perhaps I should mention that human ecology means rather different things or has different shades of meaning to different people. My own preference is for the way biologists use it, as the relationship between the human species and the total environment, the physical, biological and social environment. Sociologists tend to use the term, as I understand it, more particularly in connection with the relationships between man and his spatial distribution on the face of the earth.

Field studies on the fertility of human populations have the same objectives as clinical and laboratory studies. These are:

1. To describe the processes of fertility as a means of defining the determinants of fertility;
2. To describe and differentiate normal from abnormal fertility; and

3. To design and prove in practice methods of fertility control.

The same methods of observation and experiment are used in field studies as in clinic or laboratory. Field study extends the limit of observation from the individual to populations, and on to the ecological viewpoint of populations in their environment. (22)* Laboratory study extends observation from the individual down through smaller universes to the molecule and even to the electron. There is no hard and fast division between these three methods of study.

As a medical student I was taught to use first the naked eye, then a lens, low power of the microscope, medium, and then high power. It was good advice. At each level there is something unique to be learned. Similar levels of observation apply to field studies. The focus of attention of field studies is on populations. Within populations the unit of observation ranges from a single individual to families, households, small groups, communities and so on to states, nations, continents. The size of the populations studied ranges from a single family through a similar progression to the world. Through field study the observer can become aware of trends in time, or differences according to location or kinds of people being studied.

Laboratory and clinic studies have the great advantage of making observation in a prepared environment, like the rats which Dr. Hoagland described, thus making it possible to isolate more accurately the effect of individual variables.

Field study takes a different course, making observations and sometimes controlled experiments in the natural environment. This complicates design and interpretation, but makes it possible to become aware of variables on a wider scale of time, place and person. Instead of requiring the subject of study to submit to observation in an environment to a large extent created by the observer, the field worker requires himself to submit

* For numbered references, see Reference List on pages 96–99.

to the environment in which the phenomenon takes place naturally. Scientific field study is a logical refinement of natural history which is the first stage of all science.

The process of adapting oneself to a new environment has a challenge quite as great as that of inventing a new laboratory method or a new clinical test. This may be illustrated by a field study of fertility and fertility control in which I had a part in India.

The object of this field study was to demonstrate a change in birth rate as a consequence of a program for birth control, and to study the factors affecting fertility and population growth. (12a) As much as 83 per cent of the population of India lives in villages, so the study took place in villages. The site of the study was in the Punjab. Birth rates are measured as numbers of live births per thousand population per year, so we needed to assure ourselves of at least an accurate count of the people and of the births taking place among them. At the same time we wanted to learn all we could about the factors affecting fertility. This led us into consideration of post partum amenorrhoea and lactation, of foetal, child and maternal deaths, of birth intervals, frequency of coitus, existing practice of contraception, of the ideas of these people on how conception takes place and of the different kinds of people and their occupations and disease problems.

In this case the unit of observation was a village so there were Test or Experimental villages where contraceptive advice and materials were offered, and Control villages where birth control was not mentioned.

After preliminary study of the area, headquarters were set up in an old mission bungalow in a small town called Khanna. A village was eventually selected for an Exploratory Study and plans discussed with the village elders who made a house in the village available to the research workers. In order to make a census one needs a map and a list of households. One of the elders produced a map of the village made in 1852. Three weeks of work with a compass and a simple surveying board resulted in a usable map. Great was our astonishment when we found that the mud houses of 1852 corresponded closely to the site plan of 1954. The village watchman was our faithful co-worker as we went from house to house making the census. The older men of the village evidently enjoyed telling us its history, and on the basis of the history it was possible to construct a list of dates of well-known events which were used to fix, with more accuracy than would have been possible otherwise, dates of marriages, births and deaths, and so the present ages of the inhabitants. Some of these dates were rather striking. One was a fight between this village and the next which happened in 1923. Another was the public hanging, the last public hanging in this area, of a man in 1935. Perhaps significant to us concerned with the population problem were the events prior to 1921. The people remembered three distinct episodes of plague and the influenza epidemic of 1920. After 1921 disease problems did not enter into the calendar. From that point on notable events were the construction of the temple and the school, and the building of a well. This village calendar of events was an important refinement in this population. Most people like them do not know their age with any accuracy.

Relationships between men and women in North India are such that a woman will not talk in front of her husband. So we had women workers to visit the wives, and men workers to visit the men. At this stage the people who did this job were those who would later direct the work of others, the senior physicians, a man and a woman, and a senior Public Health Nurse.

We learned that we could expect the people of this village to give fairly reliable pregnancy histories, and that they would tell us about their understanding of the anatomy and physiology of reproduction. The women would tell our women workers about menstruation and lactation, and give information about their practice of birth control, such as it was. They did not like to be too precise about their frequency of sexual intercourse.

On enquiry from a sample of people we had got to know best we gathered that most couples would like to learn about birth control. Then we started a program of offering five methods of birth control to each husband and each wife of childbearing age. This was maintained at monthly intervals for 15 months. During this time a system was set up to find out about births, deaths and migrations.

After 9 months of experience in this exploratory village the same methods of field work were applied in two other villages, one test village where contraception was offered, and one control village where contraception was not mentioned. These villages were observed for a year as the pilot Study. The prospects for demonstrating a change in birth rate seemed high enough to justify observing a population of 8000 people with a program for contraception, and two separate Control populations of 4000 each for four years as the definitive study. Some 70,000 visits were made to these villages to give contraceptive materials and advice and to collect data. Field work ceased in 1960. No significant change in the crude birth rate was observed, although about 17% of the couples became users of birth control. (39) Data from this study are now being analyzed.

This is one example of the procedures of a field study. There are a number of others which will be discussed later. The purpose now is to examine more closely the units of observation to which these field methods are applied.

Field studies of human fertility are concerned with populations of human beings. Populations have many of the properties of individuals, organs, or cells, but they also have distinctive properties. A population exists in time and space, but unlike an individual or a cell it can grow younger as well as older, and it can grow smaller as well as larger. It can and usually does experience fertility, mortality and migration at the same time and this experience usually continues indefinitely. The birth, death and migration rates of a population are influenced not only by their numerator, the births, deaths or migrations, but also by their denominator, the base population. The birth rate of Puerto Rico has fallen in the last few years, but a considerable proportion of this change is almost certainly due to differential migration of young couples, leaving behind a higher proportion of the older and therefore less fertile couples. (33)

Field studies make it possible to study the influence of environment on a phenomenon such as fertility, and of fertility or population growth on the environment. The environment itself is more than the physical environment, the soil, temperature, humidity, altitude. There is also a biological environment — the viruses, bacteria, plants and animals which help to determine infections and nutrition. Some of these factors influence fertility directly; examples are syphilis and gonorrhoea. Further, environment includes the psychological and social factors acting on the population. Ideas, customs, fashions, values, religion and politics are all part of an environment. Indian villagers told us that these days it is government by democracy, which means counting of heads. They said, "If they have more votes than us, we shall lose power in Government, so naturally we want large families."

Such considerations lead on to the concept of ecology and the ecosystem. (22) According to this point of view the human population is one part of the greater whole which includes the physical basis of life; all other living beings and man are part of the biosphere. The ecological point of view is concerned with influences on human fertility just as real and significant as the DNA molecule or the chemical structure of steroids.

Observations on fertility made in the field are dependent on what people will report wholly or largely on their own initiative in response to questions put to them by interviewers, and to a much lesser extent on biological specimens collected in homes and on clinical observations, such as abdominal palpation. Reporting of live births is required by law in most countries today; in developed countries the level of reporting is often fairly good though usually not so good as reporting of deaths, which fairly regularly is the first part of vital statistics reporting to reach an acceptable standard. Reporting of stillbirths is less accurate and of abortions or miscarriages is usually poor. Under field conditions it is difficult to get an accurate diagnosis of early pregnancy. Until recently there was no clinical or laboratory test for pregnancy which was practical and accurate under field conditions. The recent development of a hemagglutination test for pregnancy is an important advance over report of delayed menstruation or basal temperature observation. (15) How practical it will be in the field remains to be seen, but here is a hope that we may get a good field test for pregnancy.

Because pregnancy wastage is usually under-reported, demographers and behavioral scientists use the word fertility to refer to live births, except when specifically defined. Fecundity refers to the power to conceive.

The objectives of any sound scientific study are based on valid and reasonable concepts. This applies to field studies, just as much as to clinic or laboratory studies.

When the aims and scope of a field study have been defined there comes the critical stage of choosing the population for study. Some field studies are based on follow-up of a clinic population. In this case the population is largely self-selected, and is therefore unlikely to be representative of the general population. This may not matter if the aim is to study the long term effect of a particular technical procedure such as the intrauterine insertion of a plastic coil, to find out how many such contraceptive coils drop out, the proportion of uteri that become infected, or the pregnancy rate of persons who keep the coil in for a given period of time. (31a, 31c)

Some studies are carried out using a stratified random sample of individuals. This method has many advantages. It makes it possible to build up an accurate idea of the effects of factors within a large population by collecting data from a few thousand persons. This was the method adopted for three major field studies in the U.S.A. They are called the Indianapolis Study (37), the Growth of the American Family Study (8), and the Family Growth in Metropolitan America Study. (36) In studies of this type the sample of individuals or couples is representative on the basis of the criteria originally chosen, but it does not allow much room for controlling for other characteristics which may in fact be highly important; nor does it permit study of an actual population with the interrelationships between people and their environment.

Other studies take whole populations as the unit of observation. Census operations are an example. Their limitation is that the number of factors which can be studied is severely limited by the number and nature of questions to which census enumerators can be expected to get accurate answers. Census enumerators do not usually have a social science or medical background. Decision to include or exclude any one question in a national census is a matter which involves large sums of money.

There are also studies of small populations of a few hundred or thousand people. This is somewhat like the biopsy method of studying an organ or tissue. Such studies possess the advantage that they can be used to investigate many factors at the same time, but they remain studies of small populations. Wisely chosen, such small samples may be informative as a well-selected biopsy. They make it possible to become aware of factors which are beyond the range of vision of other methods of study; one result is that they are more likely to take notes of factors not fully foreseen as important when the study was designed. An example is the finding of the Khanna Study in India that migration is a highly important factor modifying population growth in that rural area (39), the marked effect of death of a child as a determinant of birth intervals (40), and of the influence of diarrhoea among weanling children as a major cause of death. (11)

Field studies are at times the means of carrying out experiments as strictly controlled as any laboratory or clinical experiment. Classical examples are studies of the effectiveness of vaccines against whooping cough (2) or anterior poliomyelitis. (7) Field studies of fertility control in India, Puerto Rico and elsewhere have employed the same principles. (17, 39)

Findings

Far and away the largest field studies, whether measured by the number of people involved, or by time or space, are those made possible by collection of census data and vital statistics. These data provide much, if not most, of the raw material used by demographers. The U. N. Demographic Section now collects and compiles the national statistics, and publishes yearbooks setting out the data in a form comparable for the various political units. (32)

The evidence of changing fertility as we learn it from these sources is impressive and fascinating. Data becomes more unreliable as we search far back in time; but with due allowances for inaccurate data it appears that 150 years ago crude birth rates were high all over the world, and were more or less stable — with the exception of one nation, France, where the birth rate had already started to fall. (28) Between the two world wars of 1914 and 1939 alarm grew in Western countries that the innate fertility of the Western people was decreasing rapidly. The spectre was raised of a depopulated France, Britain, or the Western world. (28) Fertility as measured by live-birth rates had indeed fallen by over 50 per cent. For many years well-informed people seemed unable to believe that the change in fertility was almost entirely a matter of voluntary control of conception, not a fundamental change in fecundity, or the power to conceive. Experience of relatively high fertility in the U.S.A. since 1945 and the evidence of specially designed field studies in the U.S.A., Britain and elsewhere leave little doubt that birth control is practiced by most couples in Western countries; it is highly effective when the people wish to have no more children. (8, 20, 37)

The last 20 years have provided the striking example of Japan, where the birth rate declined in 10 years from 35 to 17. (19) In this instance the major method of birth control has been, and is, induced abortion. The agencies interested in health in Japan are now doing all they can to persuade the people to use contraception rather than induced abortion. (19)

These giant field studies covering many nations over eight or nine generations leave no doubt that fertility control is possible, and that it has been achieved by a variety of methods. Special studies indicate that the methods of birth control most widely used are *coitus interruptus,* douching, condom, induced abortion, rhythm method, and, in Ireland, postponement of marriage. (1, 5, 20, 35) Other mechanical and chemical vaginal methods, and of course oral contraceptives, account for only a small part of the total reduction in fertility. We do know how fertility has been reduced in these countries, but we have little or no proved and demonstrated answer to the question of why fertility has changed so markedly in many Western or Westernized nations. Association of lower fertility with increased education, industrialization and social mobility is highly suggestive, but it is not definite.

Essentially the same question faces us when we consider the high fertility in other nations — why is it so high? The answer that it is high because people do not know how to practice birth control or do not have access to a sufficiently simple method of birth control may well be partially true. Yet most of the fall in the birth rate of Western countries was achieved without the benefit of chemical or mechanical methods of contraception. Giving advice on birth control has always been illegal in France, and it is still illegal in Massachusetts and Connecticut today. Strictly speaking, induced abortion is illegal in Japan (19), yet in spite of social and legal pressures against birth control all these people and a great many more have managed to reduce their fertility by well over half.

Other people still have what we may consider large families. But are they having all the children they would have if they did nothing to control fertility?

These and other considerations drive us back to the point where we start to ask ourselves, what is normal human fertility, unmodified by any form of birth control?, and then the question of what the factors are which determine fertility.

Natural fertility

To take a strictly hypothetical situation, a human population with natural, uninhibited fertility would be one where cohabitation started at puberty and continued regularly until well after menopause, where there is little or no inherited or acquired disease causing sterility, where there is good nutrition and low mortality, particularly maternal and young child mortality, where the people make no attempt to prevent conception, and where they have no customs, such as periods of separation or abstinence which have the effect of increasing birth intervals. In all probability such a population has never existed. The nearest approach is some way from this ideal.

Studies on populations believed to be as near as possible to these conditions have been made. Some studies are based on data from parish registers of small stable communities in France (10), Italy (16), Canada (14), or Estonia (18) in the 18th or early 19th centuries. One used data from the Cocos-Keeling Islands in the Pacific Ocean (27), where exceptional records were kept. The Hutterite people of the Midwestern United States provide an example. (6) Data from Indian villages have been used. (16a) The French demographer, Henry, has brought much of these data together. (16b)

In brief summary it appears that at the height of the fertile age group, between the ages of 20 and 25, in any year 50 out of 100 women in the six most fertile of such populations bear a child. Fertility is such that on the average each woman has had 10 or 11 births by the time she reaches 50.

These findings are of great importance to anyone concerned to identify the factors affecting fertility. If the fertility of a population is substantially less than this there must be reasons. The reasons may be biological, such as genetically inherited infertility, an infective disease preventing conception or causing pregnancy wastage, or a high rate of endocrine disturbance perhaps as a result of iodine deficiency, or prolonged postpartum amenorrhoea.

The reasons may be of mixed biological and social origin, such as late marriage with continence before marriage, customary infrequent coitus or separation between husband and wife, possibly prolonged breast feeding, or use of contraception or induced abortion.

There are purely social considerations leading to a desire for only a few children, hence for using birth control. These include the cost of rearing and educating children and the problems of dividing hereditary land or other property among the next generation.

Social methods of fertility control include polyandry as practised by the Tibetans (30), and a combination of late marriage and a high rate of celibacy, as among the Irish. (1) Some social factors tend to encourage large families. Obvious examples are some religions, and political pressures to add individuals so that a particular group may dominate; another factor is desire for sons.

All these types of factors possibly affecting fertility may be fitted into the ecological concept.

The remainder of this paper is devoted to illustrations of how field studies have contributed to an understanding of these categories of factors which affect fertility.

Factors affecting fertility

A. *Biological Factors*

Age of the mother, and to a lesser extent of the father, is a fundamental factor determining fertility. Puberty heralds the onset of reproductive powers in both male and female. Reproductive powers cease in the female with the completion of menopause. Study of the variability in the ages at which these events occur is an obvious interest of field studies. Between these two events, measurement of maternal age specific fertility is a useful method of demonstrating how fertility changes with age. There is some evidence of relative infertility in the first few years after menarche, possibly as a result of anovulatory cycles, and again as age of menopause draws near. (3, 4, 12b) There is need for more precise studies of how age affects fertility.

The rate at which women produce live births is influenced by the events which determine birth intervals and by pregnancy wastage.

The best data on pregnancy wastage to date have been collected by field study in the Hawaiian Island of Kauai. (9)

Intervention of an abortion or miscarriage between two live births is one factor which determines live birth intervals. After delivery there are usually some months when the woman does not menstruate, and presumably when she does not ovulate. Ovulation can certainly occur without menstruation, as is proved by records of women who go many years without menstruating, yet produce numbers of children. (12b) After the usual resumption of menstruation there is a period before conception takes place which is usually fairly constant at about 6 months in the absence of use of birth control, (40) and then if there is to be a live birth there will be 8 or 9 months of gestation.

Other major factors affecting the probability of conception are frequency of coitus and use of contraception or induced abortion as methods of birth control. Lactation as a factor delaying conception may act more by inhibition of ovulation, and hence of menstruation, than by a direct effect. (31b, 31c, 40) Lactation may also be associated with a taboo on coitus, as happens in some African populations. (21)

Accurate field observations will remain one main source of data with which to study the effect of these interacting factors with useful additions from clinic studies. Dr. Vollman has gained the cooperation of most of the women in the Swiss village where he was general practitioner, getting them to record menstrual dates, conceptions and deliveries over a period of 25 years. (34) The studies in which I took part in India were the means of making monthly records of menstruation, lactation, use of contraception, separation between husband and wife, conceptions and deliveries. These data are now being analyzed. Already it is possible to show that on the average an abortion, stillbirth or live born child which dies in the first month of life is followed by conception in 10 months on the average. Whereas if the child survives a month the next conception occurs 20 months later on the average. Women who are menstruating have 8 or 9 times the probability of conceiving as compared to women who are not menstruating.

Prevalence of sterility within a population is another factor affecting fertility of a population. Study of the current rate of sterility within a population depends on definition of sterility. In order to distinguish sterile from non-sterile couples it is necessary to distinguish women who are exposed to the possibility of conception and those who are not, then to collect data to find the normal limit of time within which conception would be expected. Wives who have not conceived within that time are taken to be sterile. The primary sterility of a woman who has never conceived is distinguished from secondary sterility of a woman who has conceived once or more, but who has difficulty in conceiving thereafter. It is not always easy to distinguish biological sterility from voluntary sterility resulting from use of birth control.

B. *Biological and social factors*

Some factors affecting fertility have both biological and social elements. Examples are age at marriage or cohabitation, use of contraception, and induced abortion.

Field tests are clearly essential to determine the acceptance and effectiveness of any proposed method of contraception. Raymond Pearl developed the concept of Pregnancy Rate as a method of measuring the effectiveness of contraception. (23) Stix and Notestein developed the method in their classic *Controlled Fertility*. (29) Christopher Tietze made the useful distinction between the physiological or biological effectiveness of a contraceptive — that is, its effectiveness when used with the greatest possible care and intelligence; clinic effectiveness, as used by a group of persons who are sufficiently strongly motivated to attend a clinic, and demographic effectiveness — the net result of its use in a general population in which some couples do not use it at all, some only in a careless manner, and others who use it as carefully as they know how. Clearly the population chosen for study will affect each of these three measures. (31c)

C. *Social and psychological factors*

Consideration of the social and psychological factors affecting fertility have long been the subject of thought and field study. The Indianapolis study was designed by a distinguished group of social scientists and biostatisticians. (37) The field work in Indianapolis City was carried out in 1941. The instrument was an interview of husbands and wives, designed to investigate the relationship between fertility and fertility control of Protestant, white couples with a minimum education of eight grades. The features investigated were differential fertility; fertility planning; methods of fertility control and social and psychological factors possibly affecting fertility.

Analysis of the data went on over 17 years. The results raised more questions than they settled, but the study demonstrated clearly the degree to which contraception is practiced, and the methods of contraception used. The Growth of the American Family Study carried out by the University of Michigan and the Scripps Foundation of Miami University, Oxford, Ohio (8), and the Princeton Study on Family Growth in Metropolitan America (36) profited from the methods and findings of the Indianapolis study and developed many original ideas. The British Royal Commission on Population and the Royal College of Obstetricians and Gynecologists sponsored a somewhat similar study in 1946. (20) In Puerto Rico the studies of Hatt and of Hill, Stycos and Back used similar methods, well adapted to a different culture. (13, 17)

Another group of field studies set out to study the effect of test programs for birth control on birth rates in Asiatic countries where population problems are serious. The pioneer studies were those sponsored by the Government of India and the World Health Organization in the rural area of Ramanagaram in Mysore, India, and at the Lodi Colony in New Delhi. (38) About the same time Koya started his studies in three villages in Japan and in the Joban Coal Fields. (19) The study in Ludhiana District, Punjab, India, with which I was connected owes much to these prior studies. About the same time Baljit Singh and J. N. Sinha in Lucknow U. P. India (25, 26) carried out two field studies, one in a rural setting, and one in the city of Lucknow. A few years later, in 1957, the field study at Singur, Bengal, India, was started. Field work is still going on, but there is encouraging evidence that the birth rate in the test villages has fallen from about 45 to 37 between 1958 and 1961. (24a) Then there is a study in Taichung City in Taiwan which is under way and which Dr. Freedman, I am sure, will be telling us about. The birth rate in Taiwan had already started to fall before the study started. The study aims to test the possibility of accelerating the fall by a well-planned experiment in education and to measure the relative effect of educational methods of varying intensity and cost. (24b) Now, I am not going to pretend to go into any more detail about these studies at this time. There are other field studies in Pakistan and Ceylon. We have here with us Professor Freedman who took part in the Indianapolis study, Professor Coale who is very much connected with the Princeton study, Dr. Basu who is a field director of the Singur study, and I had experience in the Ludhiana Study, so in the time for discussion there should be ample opportunity to learn more about these studies if you wish to do so.

Summary and conclusions

Field study is an important method in the broad effort to understand the factors which determine human fertility and to prove which are the most effective and least expensive methods of fertility control.

Some of the factors affecting fertility cannot be understood apart from their ecological context. These factors range from the influence of the physical environment as climate and temperature, including their effect on nutrition, through biological factors of microörganisms and endocrine influences, to social factors such as age at marriage, desire for sons, laws of inheritance, religion and politics. Fertility is one aspect of the relation between human population growth and the environment.

Field studies range from census operations to scientifically controlled field experiments. These studies have unique contributions to make to the sum of knowledge. Together with the findings from laboratory and clinical studies a rounded understanding of the processes of human fertility becomes a feasible goal. Successful application of this knowledge towards effective control of human fertility may then become a reality.

REFERENCES

1. Arensburg, C. M., and Kimball, S. T.: *Family and Community in Ireland*. Cambridge, Mass., Harvard U. P., 1940.
2. Bell, J. A.: *Pertussis Immunization*. J. Am. Med. Ass. *137*: 1276:1948.
3. Coale, A. J., and Tye, C. Y.: *The Significance of Age Patterns of Fertility in High Fertility Populations*. Milbank Memorial Fund Quarterly. *39*:631–646:1961.
4. Collett, M. E., Wertenberger, G. E., Fiske, V. M.: *The Effect of age upon the pattern of the Menstrual Cycle*. Fertility and Sterility *5*:437–448:1954.
5. Cook, R. C.: *Human Fertility: The Modern Dilemma*. New York, Sloane, 1951.
6. Eaton, J., and Mayer, A. M.: *The Social Biology of Very High Fertility among the Hutterites. The Demography of a Unique Population*. Human Biology *25*:206–264:1953.
7. Francis, T. Jr., Napier, J. A. et al: *Evaluation of the 1954 Field Trial of Poliomyelitis Vaccine*. Final report. Ann Arbor, Michigan, 1957.
8. Freedman, R., Whelpton, P. K., Campbell, A. A.: *Family Planning, Sterility and Population Growth*. New York, McGraw-Hill, 1959.
9. French, F. E., and Bierman, J. M.: *Probabilities of Fetal Mortality*. Public Health Reports. *77*:835–847:1962.
10. Gautier, E., Henry, L.: *La Population de Crulai, paroisse normande*. Paris, Presses Universitaires de France, Table VIII pp. 149–154, 1958.
11. Gordon, J. E., Chitkara, I. D., and Wyon, J. B.: *Weanling Diarrhoea*. Am. J. Med. Sci. *245*:345–377:1963.

12a. Gordon, J. E., and Wyon, J. B.: *Field Studies in Population Dynamics and Population Control.* Am. J. Med. Sci. *240*:361–386:1960.

12b. Gordon, J. E., Wyon, J. B.: *Unpublished data, India-Harvard-Ludhiana Population Study.* Harvard School of Public Health.

13. Hatt, P. K.: *Backgrounds of Human Fertility in Puerto Rico.* Princeton University Press. 1952.

14. Henripin, J.: *La Fécondité des ménages canadiens au début du XVIIIe siècle.* Population *9*:61–84:1954.

15. Southan, A., Sultzer, B. M., and Cohen, H.: Am. J. Ob. & Gyn. *85*:495–499:1963.

16a. Henry, L.: *La Fécondité des Villages de l'Inde.* Population *15*: 144–147:1960.

16b. Henry, L.: *Some Data on Natural Fertility.* Eugenics Quarterly *8*:81–91:1961.

17. Hill, R., Stycos, J. M., Back, K. W.: *The Family and Population Control.* Chapel Hill, University of North Carolina Press, 1959.

18. Hyrenius, H.: *Fertility and Reproduction in a Swedish Population Group without Family Limitation.* Population Studies. *12*: 121–130:1958.

19. Koya, Y.: *Pioneering in Family Planning.* Population Council, New York and Japan Medical Publishers, Inc. Tokyo, 1963.

20. Lewis-Faning, E.: *Report on an Enquiry into Family Limitation and its Influence on Human Fertility during the past Fifty years.* Papers of the Royal Commission on Population. Vol. I, H.M.S.O. London, 1949.

21. Lorimer, F. et al.: *Culture and Human Fertility.* UNESCO. Paris, 1954.

22. Odum, E. P.: *Fundamentals of Ecology.* Philadelphia, 1959.

23. Pearl, R.: *The Natural History of Population.* Oxford University Press. London, 1939.

24a. Population Council (Ed): *India: The Singur Study.* Studies in Family Planning. *1*:1. The Population Council, New York. April, 1963.

24b. Population Council (Ed): *Taiwan: The Taichung Program of Prepregnancy Health.* Studies in Family Planning. *1*:10. Population Council, New York. April, 1963.

25. Singh, Baljit: *Five Years of Family Planning in the Countryside.* J. K. Institute of Sociology and Human Relations (Monograph No. 6). Lucknow University. 1958.
26. Sinha, J. N.: *Urban Fertility Patterns. A Survey in the Cities of Lucknow and Gorakhpur.* J. K. Institute of Sociology and Human Relations (Monograph No. 8). Lucknow University. 1959.
27. Smith, T. E.: *The Cocos-Keeling Islands: a demographic laboratory.* Population Studies. *14*:94–130:1960.
28. Spengler, J. J.: *France Faces Depopulation.* Durham, N.C., Duke U. Press. 1938.
29. Stix, R., and Notestein, F. W.: *Controlled Fertility.* Baltimore, 1940.
30. Thomas, L.: *Out of this World.* New York, Greystone Press, 1950.
31a. Tietze, C.: *Intra-uterine Contraceptive Devices.* Excerpta Medica International Congress Series No. *54*:9–20:1963.
31b. Tietze, C.: *The Effect of Breastfeeding on the Rate of Conception.* International Population Conference, 1961. New York.
31c. Tietze, C.: *The Use-Effectiveness of Contraceptive Methods.* pp. 357–369. *in* Kiser, C. V. (Ed.), Research in Family Planning. Princeton U. Press, 1962.
32. United Nations: *Demographic Yearbook,* New York, U.N. 1960.
33. Vazquez, Jose, L.: *Fertility Trends in Puerto Rico.* Mimeograph, Section of Biostatistics, Department of Preventive Medicine & Public Health, School of Medicine of Puerto Rico. 1962.
34. Vollman, R. F.: *The Degree of Variability of the Length of the Menstrual Cycle in Correlation with Age of Women.* Gynaecologia (Basel, Switzerland) *142*:310–314:1956.
35. Westoff, C. F., Herrera, L. F., and Whelpton, P. K.: *The Use, Effectiveness and Acceptability of Methods of Fertility Control.* Milbank Memorial Fund Quarterly *31*:291–357:1953.
36. Westoff, C. F., Potter, R. G., Sagi, P. C., Mishler, E. G.: *Family Growth in Metropolitan America.* Princeton University Press. 1961.
37. Whelpton, P. K., Kiser, C. V. (Eds.): *Social and Psychological Factors affecting Fertility.* Milbank Memorial Fund. New York. 5 Vols. 1946, 1950, 1952, 1954, 1958.

38. World Health Organization: *Final Report on Pilot Studies in Family Planning, two Vols.* W.H.O. S.E. Asia Regional Office. New Delhi, 1954.
39. Wyon, J. B. and Gordon, J. E.: *A Long Term Prospective-type Field Study of Population Dynamics in the Punjab, India.* pp. 17–32, *in* Kiser, C. V. (Ed.): Research in Family Planning. Princeton U. Press. 1962.
40. Wyon, J. B., Potter, R. G., New, M. L. and Gordon, J. E.: *Duration of Lactation, Amenorrhoea and Interpregnancy Intervals.* Report to the Population Association of America annual meeting. Philadelphia, April, 1963.

DISCUSSION

DR. HISAW: It is perfectly obvious that the problem that confronts us is not a simple one. The social factors that have been mentioned and brought out are many. The problem calls for consideration by all branches of the social sciences that can be brought to bear on this particular subject. I wonder about one thing. One of my friends, a historian, tells me that it requires about four generations to break the established pattern of thought in a revolutionary conception. That is, people have to be born, people have to die and it takes about four generations for one of these conceptions to become established. When we think of the many different economic, political, religious, and other conceptions that are brought to bear on the problem in hand, I wonder if the social scientists can in some way, give us a prognostication as to the probable outcome of our efforts in finding a solution to the population problem. Do they think it will require four generations, will it be a thousand years, can it ever be done, do they have a gloomy attitude towards this, are they optimistic, and so on. I am just speaking as a biologist but am sure many would enjoy having the opinions of social scientists on this point. Is there any discussion?

DR. PINCUS: Do we have what we might call a general rule concerning the relationship of age to fertility and fecundity? From these various studies are there obvious indications of racial or genetic differences?

DR. WYON: I think there are probably other people who can answer this question better than I. Dr. Coale and Dr. Freedman are more acquainted with this literature. It seems to me there is evidence that from the age of menarche to about the age of 18 or 20 in the female there is a gradual rise in fertility. And again from the age of, let us say, 35 there seems to be some evidence of the gradual sloping off of fertility until fertility, or fecundability, finally ceases. As of this date the evidence is not very good. What I was really doing was pleading for better evidence on this, on factors such as use of birth control and frequency of coitus. At the later ages, when women mostly have had enough children, these behavioral factors may enter in, and are very difficult to record accurately.

DR. COALE: I think Dr. Wyon has given us an adequate answer. The best collection of data on this that I know of appears in two or three articles that have been written by Henry, a French demographer. He has collected all the data he could lay his hands on that indicated the level of fertility in the absence of deliberate attempts to control it. These data show a similar curve for most populations that have been observed under these circumstances, with the peak fecundity (that is, the probability of conception in the absence of control) at ages 20 to 24, preceded by a rise from menarche and then gradually falling off after age 25. The fall accelerates in the thirties, the mean age of the last conception being probably short of 40. In some individual cases, however, the last child is conceived at age 50 or later. The difficulty in trying to determine what differences there are among these curves, racial or what have you, depends on such imponderables as yet unstraightened out as the age of the first cohabitation, which could have an effect on later fertility, and the influence of lactation and the likelihood in any given population that various techniques of interference will be employed by the end of the childbearing period.

DR. ASTWOOD: You mentioned, in your field study of three Indian villages, that contraception was advised in only one and there was no difference in fertility between these three; could you tell us what sort of contraception was advised or practiced?

DR. WYON: The progression was that we started off in one village where we offered five different methods of birth control: rhythm method, *coitus interruptus,* foam tablet, salt solution and cotton pad, and a contraceptive paste and cotton pad; these were all selected on the principle that they did not require the intervention of a doctor or nurse, thinking that if one of these should prove to be effective on a population basis they could be used widely throughout villages in India. Then the next stage was where we had two villages, one experimental village where we offered birth control and one where we did not. And then later on we had seven villages where we offered birth control, a total population of 8,000, and 8 villages where we did not. Now, by this time we had established to our satisfaction that the foam tablet was the method of birth control of choice among these people and that rhythm and *coitus interruptus* were already used to a certain extent before we ever went there. So the methods of birth control promoted in the birth control villages were foam tablets, rhythm and *coitus interruptus.* Measured by crude birth rate there was no difference in fertility. When we examined just those parts of the women's pregnancy history when the couples were using birth control there was a very distinct difference, something of the order of 60 per cent between times when they were using birth control as contrasted with comparable controls. In other words, the contraceptive was effective; the question was use of the method by a sufficient proportion of the population.

DR. TIETZE: Since this is a mixed company, by which I mean biologists and social scientists, it is necessary to point out one of the most deplorable examples of lack of communication that concerns the use of the term "fertility." When biologists speak of fertility they mean the capacity to reproduce. When demographers speak of fertility they refer to reproduction achieved and not to capacity. If they mean capacity, they speak of fecundity. This discrepancy of usage between biologists and demographers, and the sharp distinction between fertility and fecundity of which the demographers have made a professional shibboleth, constitutes a most fertile source of misunderstanding. All of us should watch ourselves very carefully and state whether we speak in the capacity of a biologist or in the capacity of a demographer. A person who, like myself, belongs to both professions must be particularly careful.

DR. PARKES: I want to emphasize this same point, this confusion between the use of the word "fertility" by biologists (to mean the capacity to bear living young) and the demographic use. On the occasion of the Royal Commission of Population in Great Britain in 1944, we had a committee sitting on this matter for three years. They arrived at no conclusions, for the simple reason that we tried to be fair and the committee consisted of biologists, gynecologists and demographers, and there seems to be a complete schism on the use of the word "fertility" which I think is very unfortunate. Dr. Wyon referred to the fall in fertility in Western Europe during the last century. Well, to a biologist (he also went on of course to say that was due to birth control) that is not necessarily at all a fall in fertility so I would like very much to emphasize and to support what Dr. Tietze said.

DR. HISAW: Thank you Dr. Parkes. You not only emphasized but you helped elucidate this point.

MRS. ALLYN H. RULE: I am wondering just how comparative methods of birth control are received in some illiterate populations and how effective communication can be in this situation.

DR. WYON: I can speak with assurance about people of one part of the Indian subcontinent. In India in general there is little or no objection to birth control or very little organized effort to try to stop birth control being talked about or birth control information given to other people. In Pakistan the situation is somewhat different. We have colleagues here at the moment in the Harvard School of Public Health who tell us of organized opposition in some places in Pakistan; they speak from personal experience. In India the question is not opposition, it's a question of whether they want to use birth control at all. In the first village, we went around to the people we knew best and asked them if they wanted to learn about birth control. Almost all of them said, "Yes, it is just what we want." Before we even mentioned birth control some people were spontaneously saying, "You know the best thing you can do for us is to teach our women how to have fewer babies." When we went around and offered birth control, 40 per cent of all the couples with a wife of childbearing age took the method and promised they would use it. But in the first year, only about 10 or 12 per cent of the total, that is ten out of these forty, did actually use the method. Over a period of four years something like 50 per cent of the couples where the wife was of childbearing age did use some method of birth control. Of those about half used it for only a month or two, so the question is not one of opposition, it is a question of understanding and realizing what the point of birth control is. We made all the efforts that we knew how during this time that we were in intimate contact with these people, meeting them month after month, to try to persuade them to use birth control. The more we went on, the more we realized that the type of arguments that appeal to us just didn't appeal to them. My conclusion is that we have to learn far more about these people, to appreciate in fact what babies mean or what children mean to them, so that we can talk their language. We are the ignorant people, not they.

ELLEN M. STAHLE: I wonder if any consideration has been given to the relationship between the biological definition of fertility and nutrition. What would be the result of a change in nutrition in one specific area or a significant difference in the usual intake in two separate areas?

DR. WYON: A Mr. De Castro, who was chairman of the Food and Agricultural Organization of the United Nations, wrote a book called, *The Geography of Hunger.* In this book he contrasted countries of high birth rate and low consumption of protein with countries of low birth rate and a high consumption of protein and drew the conclusion that low protein in the diet was the cause of high birth rate. However, if one cares to go to the same sources that he went to, one can draw another selection of countries that show entirely the opposite relationship. As far as I know there's really very little evidence of the direct effect of malnutrition causing subfertility in the biological sense.

MR. WILLIAM DYSON: Our speaker referred to three sets of variables having an effect on fertility. First of all were those of the medical field, then those of the socio-medical; in both instances the speaker set up several examples. Yet when he came to the social variables, he did not give us any listing of what some of these social variables might be. I wonder if he would like to expand on what some of these variables are.

DR. WYON: By social factors, I was thinking of factors which have a direct influence on fertility as measured by live births, or even an indirect influence on fertility as measured by live births, which are quite apart from any bodily act. Contraception is an act which requires use of the intellect and also some manipulation of bodily function. Whereas the age at which a person gets married is something which is not immediately involved in the act of coitus, late age at marriage may involve abstention from the act. So this is an example that I would categorize as purely a social factor affecting live birth rates. Then obviously there are other social correlates which perhaps are what you have in mind, such as: education, occupation, social class; in India, caste. For your interest, in the villages where we worked we can show a differential fertility by caste. Is this the type of thing you had in mind?

MR. DYSON: Yes. May I ask what kind of data you have to show us what the impact of these variables is?

DR. WYON: In terms of our particular data we have studied caste, education and, to a certain extent, occupation. Caste is certainly associated with differential fertility. Evidence on the other two factors is not yet certain. Then, there is the experience of the husband outside the village; experience in the army or working in a big city is another possible way of differentiating people who possibly knew more about birth control than other members of the village population. I think these are the main things in our particular study.

DR. STEVEN PLANK: Referring to the question of the effect of nutrition on fertility, two reports come to mind. One is that of Kamat[1] on a study in Bombay of differential fertility between two groups where nutrition was considered the principal variable. The better-fed women had more children with shorter intervals

[1] Kamat, M. and Kamat, R. G., "Diet and Fecundity in India," in Proceedings of the 6th International Conference on Planned Parenthood, 1959.

between births, shorter periods of post-partum amenorrhea, and a higher frequency of intercourse. Kamat also referred to a number of other studies on animals and humans which showed a depression of libido and fertility when nutrition was poor.

The second is a report by a committee of nutritionists of the FAO[2]. They found an association between low nutritional levels and a high occurrence of premature births, abortions, and still-births. In terms of population growth, a stillbirth, an abortion, or a premature birth with its high risk of early death are quite different from a full-term child with opportunity to survive to maturity. Nutrition, then, again appears to affect fertility — in the demographer's sense.

[2] WHO Chronicle 16:445, 1962.

CHANGING FERTILITY IN TAIWAN

RONALD FREEDMAN

Professor of Sociology and Director, University of Michigan Population Center.

TAIWAN is an especially interesting example of the developing areas in which fertility (demographers' definition) is high, because many of the conditions believed to be necessary for a fertility decline appear to be present there. In fact, a fertility decline has already begun in Taiwan. Its unusually good statistics, for an area of this kind, make it possible to observe this change as it occurs and to initiate experimental studies which may accelerate the changes under way.

If Taiwan is to be viewed as an example of a high fertility population, it is necessary first to sketch in broad terms the relevant characteristics of high fertility countries. This involves some very general ideas about the sociology of human fertility.[1] Dr. Wyon has already covered this in part, and I will be poaching to some extent on the territory of Dr. Du Bois who will close the conference, but I need to say something about these general ideas so that the case of Taiwan may illustrate general principles.

First of all, high fertility and high mortality have gone together historically. It is still true that most high fertility countries have relatively high mortality. Low mortality in association with high

---

[1] For a much more complete treatment see the author's "The Sociology of Human Fertility" in *Current Sociology*, Vol. X/XI, No. 2, 1961–62, pp. 35–121.

fertility characterizes only a few countries (including Taiwan) and this is almost entirely a postwar development.

Secondly, most high fertility countries are socially and economically underdeveloped as compared with low fertility countries. What do we mean by underdeveloped? One of the most important characteristics of almost all underdeveloped countries is the great importance of family and kinship ties. Many, if not all, of the crucial social relationships involve relations with kinfolk in such societies, while in developed societies other types of impersonal relations or at least relations not based on kinship are dominant. An obvious example is the fact that economic activity is carried on mainly by kinship units of some kind in underdeveloped but not developed societies. But this applies also to a wide range of activities: recreation, social security, protection and so forth.

Broadly speaking, development is related to many other variables: urbanization, industrialization, more complex technology, greater capital investment per worker, higher living standards, and greater literacy. There is an increase in the mass media of communication and in transportation facilities which go with larger markets and linkage of local populations in larger social, political and economic units. In the larger units, a more complex division of labor exists not only with respect to economic life but also in almost every other aspect. Thus, the tasks of an urban society in a developed society are divided among a much larger number of institutions. As the economic unit ceases to be the family, recruitment of workers is less closely linked to reproduction. I want to suggest that what is essential in the development process is the shift from major dependence on relatively self-contained local institutions, to dependence on larger social, economic, and political units. Such a shift implies a change in the division of labor from one in which the family or kinship unit is necessarily central to a larger complex in which such local units as family and village give up many functions or activities to larger nonfamilial specialized units. In such a shift, greater literacy and the development of effective communication networks are essential. So a key characteristic of high fertility societies is that they are "underdeveloped" in the sense that social and individual needs are largely met in local familial and community units on which people are relatively isolated from outside contacts.

A third characteristic of the high fertility countries is that they have very young age distributions — a high proportion of children and a small proportion of older people. This is true whether mortality is low or high. This results in what appears to be a paradox to most people: when mortality falls in high fertility countries and people live longer, the proportion of children increases and the proportion of older people doesn't. I will leave the explanation of this paradox for the discussion period. It is a fact that where mortality falls the resulting great increase in population growth means first of all a very large increase in the numbers of children for whom education, health and other expensive social services need to be founded. I will leave the discussion of the economic aspects of this development to Professor Coale. I do want to point out now, however, that when mortality falls so most children survive, the pressure on housing and on many social and economic arrangements becomes very great in a society whose organization is adjusted historically to smaller families with many children dying.

The fact is that a fall in mortality almost always precedes the transition to lower fertility. This means that population growth increases greatly and at the same time the population not only continues to have large numbers of young dependents but also the proportion of such dependents even increases. What is often called the demographic transition is the shift from high death rates and birth rates to low death rates and birth rates. The process almost always has involved first a fall in the death rate and then a fall in the birth rate after a lag of some time. The crucial question now is how short this lag can be made.

Now, what is the explanation for the existence of high fertility over most of man's history and in most of the world's population today? There are many theories, but I think many, if not most, demographers and sociologists would agree on two fundamental explanations:

1. Fertility tends to be high in a society in which the goals that are highly valued in that society are achieved through kinship or other family ties rather than through other social relationships. If the things worth having are obtained through relatives and children, children will be highly valued and fertility will be relatively high.

2. If mortality is high and variable, extra children will be borne in order to insure the survival of the essential minimum number. If the crucial things in life depend on having children, customs develop to maximize the probability that some children will survive to adulthood. If male children are especially important — as they are in many societies — then the necessity of insuring the survival of male children pushes fertility even higher.

The importance of mortality is that high fertility does not always mean large families. For example, an Indian study[2] which found that the average married woman had 5 to 6 children by age 35–44 also found that the number of their children still alive at that time averaged 3 to 4.

Suggestions in some quarters that a fall in fertility should be sought before a fall in mortality are poor counsels in my opinion. In general, a fall in mortality is a precondition for a fall in fertility where family and children have been of crucial importance.

Dr. Wyon has already indicated that fertility is not uniformly high in underdeveloped areas. I would like to stress that again. What I am calling high fertility covers a considerable range and is associated with many different customs limiting fertility

[2] United Nations, *The Mysore Population Study*. New York: The United Nations, 1962.

directly and indirectly. Still it is true that almost invariably fertility is relatively high where people depend on familial and local units and where mortality is high.

I haven't listed the absence of contraceptives as an important cause for high fertility. I don't believe their unavailability has been of importance until recently, because the social situation and high mortality led to a high valuation of fertility. Couples had more babies, because they learned to want them for the rewards in the society — not because they were ignorant of how to avoid having them. All this changes with lower mortality and changes in the basic social situation, but these basic ideas are new and in most developing countries neither complete nor old enough to have affected basic values and behaviors deeply.

With this very general background, we can now consider Taiwan.[3] Before discussing the fertility data, a brief reference to the considerable social and economic development that has already occurred in Taiwan is relevant as essential background. I find that most people are aware of the military and international political situation with respect to Taiwan but have no knowledge about the internal domestic situation and the standard of living. Not only has there been considerable change in the last decade, but the levels reached in many important indices of modernization and development are much higher than are found in most other developing high fertility countries.

Conditions are favorable for a fertility decline if high rates for the following are pertinent: literacy, education, urbanization,

---

[3] The data reported here are drawn from studies of the Taiwan Population Studies Center, of which the author is co-director with Dr. T. C. Hsu, Commissioner of Health for Taiwan. The associate directors are Dr. C. L. Chen and Dr. Y. Takeshita. Much of the material in this paper is adapted from "Fertility Trends in Taiwan: Tradition and Change" appearing in *Population Studies* for March, 1963. That article was jointly written by the author and Dr. J. Y. Peng, Dr. Y. Takeshita, and Mr. T. H. Sun.

non-agricultural employment, newspaper circulation and communication via the mails. Table 1 shows changes in these indications from 1952 to 1961. In each case (except for the per cent living in large cities) it would be possible to demonstrate that the levels attained by 1961 in Taiwan are far higher than the average for most developing high-fertility countries.

We can cite as only one example the circulation of daily newspapers per 1000 in some high fertility countries:

Taiwan (1959)	— 49	Korea (1958)	— 57
Ceylon (1958)	— 20	Burma (1960)	— 12
India (1960)	— 11	Cambodia (1960)	— 6
Iran (1959)	— 5	Indonesia (1959)	— 5

The extremely favorable health and mortality situation is also very relevant. Crude death rates fell slowly but steadily under the Japanese rule from about 33 at the beginning of the century to 19 in 1940–1943. After the war there was a rapid fall in mortality with the crude death rate reaching 8 by 1957.[4] Life expectancy is now somewhere between 60 and 65 years. Most parents can now expect all their children to survive to adulthood. This situation has existed in Taiwan for some years now, so that there probably is a general awareness of it in the population. In a recent survey in Taichung, we probed this question in an interview with 1300 mothers from 20 to 39 years old. The overwhelming majority were aware of the change in mortality that had occurred. The necessity of bearing large numbers of children in order to have the smaller desired number survive to adulthood is no longer present in this situation. Taiwan is one of the high-fertility countries in which the mortality-decline part of the demographic revolution is an actuality. The low mortality and other indicators of social change are all

---

[4] It is likely that these official rates are too low by several points, because there is significant under-registration of infant mortality.

TABLE 1

Trends in Some Indices of Social Development for Taiwan (1952–1961)

YEAR	% living in 5 largest cities[a]	% over 12 literate M	F	% over 12 completed primary education M	F	% over 12 with education beyond primary school M	F	Per capita circulation of daily newspapers[d]	Per capita postings of domestic mails per year[d]	% male labor force over 12 in non-agricultural occupations[g]
1952	18	b	b	53c	28c	17	7	28	8	44
1958	20	60	40	60	35	23	10	43	31	49
1961	21	63	44	63	40	26	12	49e	33f	52

a Unless otherwise noted, all data are from the publications of the Department of Civil Affairs, Province of Taiwan and are based on the register of population.

b Unavailable.

c For 1952, it was necessary to assume that only persons over 12 had completed primary school.

d Data from United Nations *Statistical Yearbook.*

e For 1959.

f For 1960.

g Excludes students, those engaged in "household management" and those listed as having no occupation.

favorable on *a priori* grounds to a decline in fertility. I will turn in a moment to evidence that such a decline has begun and is likely to accelerate. Before doing so, I want to direct your attention briefly to some consequences of the sharp reduction in mortality while fertility has remained high. In Table 2 you can see in the data on natural increase that the rate per 1,000 reached the very high level of 37 in 1952 and was still about 30 in 1961. Such a rate of increase — 3 per cent per year — means a doubling of population every 27 years and Taiwan is already one of the most densely populated countries in the world.

The high fertility and low mortality also gives Taiwan a very young age distribution — even younger now than it was 10 years ago. Panel B in Table 9 compares the age-distribution of Taiwan with that of England and Wales. Note that one-third of Taiwan's population is under 10 years of age as compared with 10 per cent in England and Wales; 53 per cent are under 20 as compared with 30 per cent in England and Wales.

So Taiwan has the low mortality, the rapid population growth and young age structure, and the type of social and economic development that might lead to a fertility decline. What is the story on fertility?

TABLE 2

Some General Demographic Trend Data for Taiwan

Date	Population (millions)	Date	Birth Rate	Death Rate	Natural Increase
			(Rates per 1000 population)		
1905	3.0	1906–10	42	33	9
1940	5.9	1936–40	45	21	24
1952	7.9	1952	47	10*	37
1961	11.3	1961	38	8*	30

* These rates and possibly the earlier ones are underestimates, because there is an underregistration of infant deaths, especially when the death occurs shortly after birth. Correcting for this fact, however, would increase the death rate by only one or two points.

TABLE 3
Fertility Rates and % Change, 1958–1961

	% change 1958–61	Rates per 1000 1958	1961
Crude Birth Rate	−8%	42	38
Total Fertility Rate	−9%	6050	5585
Age-Specific Rates			
15–19	+5%	43	45
20–24	0	248	248
25–29	+2%	336	341
30–34	−12%	281	246
35–39	−22%	199	156
40–44	−21%	90	71
45–49	−28%	14	10

Various measures of fertility indicate a decline in fertility in each year from 1958 to 1961 — amounting in all to about 8 per cent (Table 3). The decline is not yet great, but its character is significant in several ways. First of all it has occurred throughout the island — in each of the 22 administrative units into which Taiwan is divided.

Secondly, the age-specific birth rates — births per 1000 women in each age group — show an important pattern. There is no decline for women below age 30, but beyond this age the older the women the sharper the decline. This is exactly what we would expect, if couples were beginning to do something about limiting family size after about 10 years of married life — when many couples have 3 or 4 or more surviving children under present mortality conditions. This is also the pattern which characterized early fertility decline in such Western countries as England.

Third, fertility is lowest where social and economic conditions are favorable to lower fertility. Note in Table 4 that fertility is lowest in the cities and highest in the countryside.

TABLE 4
Fertility Rates by Type of Place: 1958

	Crude Birth Rate	Gen. Fertility Rate	Total Fertility Rate
Cities	39.5	173	5420
Towns	40.5	180	5935
Countryside	42.1	188	6372

For the 22 areas we found that fertility tended to be lower the higher the per cent of literacy, the higher the per cent with more than primary education, the higher the per cent in non-agricultural employment, the greater the number of letters posted per capita — all indicators of a wider network of communications and interdependence and of less dependence on local community and familial institutions. It is symbolic — as well as humorous — that the greatest negative correlation with fertility is found for long-distance telephone calls per capita!

I would like to turn now to another type of evidence that leads us to believe that the present fertility decline is likely to accelerate and that it is based on a strong desire to limit the number of children to a moderate number and by modern methods.

Data from two interview surveys in the city of Taichung are consistent with the island-wide results from the official statistics. They indicate attitudes and behavior consistent with the fertility decline that has occurred already and also with a prediction of continuing and possibly accelerating decline in the future. The surveys indicate: (1) a strong consensus in the population that a moderate size family is desirable; (2) widespread approval of family planning and actual use of family planning by a significant minority of the population; (3) while expressing "modern" ideas about family planning, the population also expresses a strong preference for sons and approval of such traditional Chinese institutions as the joint family and the dependence of older parents on their children.

Taichung is the provincial capital of Taiwan. It has a population of 300,000 — but this includes 100,000 living on farms in the rural edge of the city. The survey data are from an early pilot study of 241 couples with a wife 25–29 and from a larger sample of about 2,400 couples representing all couples in Taichung with a wife 20–39 years old. Only the smaller sample has been intensively analyzed so far, but the preliminary results of the larger samples are completely consistent with it.

The couples want a moderate number of children (see Table 5). To be childless is an unspeakable tragedy. One child is very undesirable. Two children are acceptable to a small num-

TABLE 5
Some Preliminary Results from Samples of 2433 Wives
20–39 Years Old: Taichung Taiwan (Nov. 1962–Jan. 1963)

A. *No. of mothers who want no more children, by present no. of children:*

No. of children in family	Mothers who prefer no more
2	20%
3	53%
4	77%
5	89%
6	92%
7+	96%

B. *No. of children wanted if could have just ideal no. for self:*

percentage distribution.		
0 or 1	—	0
2	—	7
3	—	30
4	—	42
5	—	13
6 or more		7
Indeterminate		1
		100%

C. *Comparison of no. of sons and daughters wanted*
— attitude of wife:

Prefer more sons than daughters:	44%
Prefer more daughters than sons:	0%*
Would like equal number:	50%
Indeterminate:	6%
	100%

* less than 0.5 per cent

D. *Relation of no. of sons and children in present family to wife's desire for more children (from a pilot study of 241 couples — May, 1962):*

Two children		Three or more children	
No sons	86%	No sons	79%
1 son	83%	1 son	64%
2 sons	58%	2 sons	20%
		3 sons	8%

E. *Use of various forms of family limitation:*

Approve idea of family planning	92%
Have ever used contraception	32%
Currently using contraception	18%
Have had 1 or more induced abortions	
Total sample	9%
Women 30–39	14%
Husband or wife sterilized	
Total sample	8%
Women 33–39	16%

ber; three or four are the model categories desired by most. Only 20 per cent want 5 or more children. Note also (in panel A of Table 5) that the number of mothers preferring no more children increases very rapidly with number of children — reaching 77 per cent among those with 4 children. The results for the responses of the husband are very similar. Similar results are obtained whether the question refers to the additional children the couples want, the number they would have if they could start over, or the number they consider ideal for other Taiwanese. There is nothing in any of these data to support the idea that the high Taiwanese fertility goes now with a desire for large numbers of children. There is also little evidence that many believe that the number of children wanted is up to God, up to fate, or otherwise not a subject for discussion and decision.

There are a variety of indications that a strong preference for sons is still deeply held. The ideal family is seen as the one with 4 children and 2 sons. Something of the preference for sons is illustrated in the data in panels C and D of Table 5. After the wives were asked how many children they wanted, they were asked how many of the desired number they would want to be girls and how many boys. About half indicated a preference for an equal number — usually in connection with a choice of 4 children. But among the rest 44 per cent preferred more sons than daughters and *none* preferred more daughters than sons. In the pilot study data, we have related the desire to have more children to the number of sons and children in the present family. It is clear that the desire for additional children decreases very rapidly with the number of sons — 2 sons is a particularly critical number.

While a moderate number of children is desired, the fact is that data from our larger sample indicate that by the time they reach the age groups 30–34 or 35–39 many women have more than the desired number. We have noted that only 20 per cent of the women considered 5 or more children as ideal for themselves, but by ages 30 to 34, 36 per cent had 5 or more and by age 35–39, 56 per cent had 5 or more. Most of the women at ages 35–39 who had 5 or more children wanted 4 or less.

As we have already indicated, to have 1 or preferably 2 sons is regarded as very important. In our larger sample of couples 20–39 years old the proportion who have at least 1 living son is 60 per cent at age 20–24 and 89 per cent by the early 30's —

the proportion who have at least 2 living sons is 17 per cent at age 20–24, 44 per cent at age 25–29, 68 per cent at 30–34 and 74 per cent by age 35–39. In short, by the time women are in their early 30's and often earlier, they have the children and the sons they want.

With this background, it is not too surprising that the overwhelming majority of the wives expressed approval of the idea of family planning (see panel E of Table 5). Almost one-third — 32 per cent — have used some form of family planning at one time or another and 18 per cent were using it at the time of interview. However, many used ineffective methods or used effective methods poorly, and many interested in the idea of family planning indicated ignorance of methods or of where to obtain information. It is not too surprising that under these conditions many resort to methods that they themselves say are undesirable. Nine per cent of all wives and 14 per cent among those 30–39 reported one or more induced abortions, although these are illegal and most women said they were undesirable. Eight per cent of all the wives and 16 per cent of those 35–39 indicated they or their husbands or both had been sterilized.

These data on desires and practices to date in the field of family limitation are consistent with the decline in fertility shown by the official statistics — and particularly the decline at ages 30 and above. There is also informal evidence of various kinds on the sale of contraceptives in the drugstores, and in the number of people coming to family planning clinics where they are available in about 100 of the 362 health districts on the island.

The rather modern ideas about family size and family planning are not associated with any widespread repudiation of traditional Chinese family values. We have already noted the strong preference for sons. There is also little indication that the new methods are desired to avoid having children or to have only one. Everyone wants at least 2 children and most want 3 or 4. Moreover (as Table 6 indicates), the couples still expect to live with their children in their old age or otherwise to be supported by them. Ideally they would like to have several sons living together in the traditional joint family. My interpretation of the situation is that they want to use modern methods under

TABLE 6

*Attitudes of Wives and Husbands to Traditional Chinese
Values About Relationship to Children*
(From May Pilot Study)

Do you expect to live with your children in your old age? Would you say:

	Wife	Husband
Definitely Yes	64%	47%
Probably Yes	14	15
Uncertain	18	29
Probably No	2	5
Definitely No	2	2
Not Ascertained	—	2
TOTAL	100%	100%

If you did not live with your children in your old age, would you expect them to bear most of your expenses of living anyway? Would you say:

	Wife	Husband
Definitely Yes	59%	34%
Probably Yes	14	14
Uncertain	15	34
Probably No	9	13
Definitely No	3	3
Not Ascertained	—	2
TOTAL	100%	100%

If you have two or more grown sons when you are older, would you like them to live with you in a large household after they are married if they can get along together? Would you say that is:

	Wife	Husband
Very Desirable	66%	52%
Desirable	18	21
Undesirable	16	25
Not Ascertained	—	2
TOTAL	100%	100%

modern conditions to achieve a traditional Chinese family. As in many other situations, the adjustment sought is one that will preserve cherished old ways as far as possible.

In Table 7 are contained a large variety of data on fertility attitudes and behavior in relation to many characteristics from the small pilot study. I won't attempt to cover them all. Let me just point out a few major trends: (1) a moderate-size family is desired by every social stratum or subgroup considered; (2) a majority of couples in all subgroups approve the idea of family planning; (3) the largest variation between subgroups is in the proportions who have actually used family planning — that is, agreement on ideals and values is close, but on behavior the differences are great. It takes something special to move people from desire to action; (4) those characteristics of the couples indicating significant knowledge or contact with the communications network of the modern world community are most closely related to wanting smaller families, greater approval of family planning, and especially to the greater practice of family planning. Note especially in sections 2, 3, and 4 of the Table the strong relation between use of family planning and the amount of education or the frequency of reading newspapers. Note also that the approval of family planning and its use is much greater if the husband is employed by non-relatives (an impersonal, modern relationship) than if he is employed by relatives or self-employed (self-employment is likely to involve a small family enterprise). This is exactly the kind of thing I had in mind when I was talking about the connection between kinship and economic activity and fertility.

It is significant that the ownership of modern consumer objects is much more closely related than total family expenditures to the use of family planning and to the number of births to date. This suggests that how much a family has or spends is less important than whether the expenditures are on consumer items characteristic of the modern world community.

TABLE 7

Practice of Family Planning, Attitudes to Family Planning, Desired Number of Children,
Number of Children Considered Ideal, by the Characteristics of the Couple
(Pilot Study of 241 couples — May, 1962)

Characteristics of the couple	No. of couples	% who have practiced some form of family planning	% with both husband & wife approving family planning unconditionally	Average number of children wanted by		Average number of children considered ideal for Taiwan		Average number of children born to date of interview
				Wife[a]	Husband[a]	Wife[a]	Husband[a]	
1. Total sample	241	34	69	3.7	3.8	4.0	3.9	2.9
2. Husband's education								
No formal education	10	0	51	4.3	4.6	4.3	3.9	3.3
Some primary school	19	16	74	3.5	3.5	4.3	3.8	2.7
Comp. primary school	89	15	64	3.9	4.0	4.0	4.2	3.1
Junior schl. level	49	41	67	3.9	3.7	3.9	3.9	2.9
Senior level graduates or more	74	62	78	3.4	3.6	3.8	3.7	2.6
3. Wife's education								
No formal education	33	9	55	4.2	3.9	4.3	4.2	3.5
Some primary school	49	20	47	3.6	3.9	4.0	4.1	2.9
Comp. primary school	85	26	79	3.8	3.9	3.9	3.9	2.9
Junior schl. level	50	60	74	3.5	3.8	4.0	3.8	2.7
Senior level graduates or more	24	71	83	3.1	3.5	3.5	3.6	2.2

TABLE 7 (Cont.)

Characteristics of the couple	No. of couples	% who have practiced some form of family planning	% with both husband & wife approving family planning unconditionally	Average number of children wanted by		Average number of children considered ideal for Taiwan		Average number of children born to date of interview
				Wife[a]	Husband[a]	Wife[a]	Husband[a]	
4. Frequency of Newspaper Reading — Husband								
Nothing in last month	33	9	52	4.4	4.2	4.3	4.4	3.4
Sometimes	16	19	62	3.9	4.0	4.2	4.2	2.9
Once or twice a week	41	5	63	3.7	4.0	4.0	3.8	2.8
Every day	146	50	76	3.7	3.7	3.9	3.8	2.7
Not ascertained	5	—	—	—	—	—	—	—
5. Frequency of Newspaper Reading — Wife								
Nothing in last month	127	19	60	3.9	3.9	4.1	4.1	3.1
Sometimes	12	33	92	3.5	4.1	3.6	3.7	2.7
Once or twice a week	29	41	86	3.5	3.6	3.9	4.1	2.4
Every day	72	58	75	3.5	3.7	3.8	3.7	2.7
Not ascertained	1	—	—	—	—	—	—	—
6. Type of family								
Joint	37	27	60	3.8	3.9	3.8	3.9	2.8
Stem	73	27	69	3.8	4.0	3.9	4.1	2.7
Nuclear	131	40	73	3.8	3.7	4.0	3.8	3.0

TABLE 7 (Cont.)

Characteristics of the couple	No. of couples	% who have practiced some form of family planning	% with both husband & wife approving family planning unconditionally	Average number of children wanted by		Average number of children considered ideal for Taiwan		Average number of children born to date of interview
				Wife[a]	Husband[a]	Wife[a]	Husband[a]	
7. Husbands' expectation to live with children								
Def. or prob. yes	149	30	69	3.9	3.8	4.0	4.0	3.0
Uncertain	69	39	70	3.8	3.8	3.9	3.7	2.6
No	18	50	83	3.4	3.6	3.9	3.7	2.6
Not ascertained	5	—	—	—	—	—	—	—
8. Husbands' attitude to joint family								
Very desirable	125	27	68	3.9	3.9	4.1	4.1	3.1
Desirable	51	37	61	3.8	3.8	3.9	3.6	2.7
Undesirable	60	47	80	3.7	3.7	3.8	3.8	2.6
Not ascertained	5	—	—	—	—	—	—	—
9. Husbands' expectation of support from children								
Def. or prob. yes	116	25	67	4.0	4.0	4.0	4.0	3.2
Uncertain	81	33	70	3.6	3.7	4.0	3.9	2.5
No	39	64	74	3.5	3.4	4.0	3.6	2.7
Not ascertained	5	—	—	—	—	—	—	—

TABLE 7 (*Cont.*)

Characteristics of the couple	No. of couples	% who have practiced some form of family planning	% with both husband & wife approving family planning unconditionally	Average number of children wanted by Wife[a]	Average number of children wanted by Husband[a]	Average number of children considered ideal for Taiwan Wife[a]	Average number of children considered ideal for Taiwan Husband[a]	Average number of children born to date of interview
10. Wife's expectation to live with children								
Def. or prob. yes	187	29	67	3.8	3.9	4.0	4.0	2.9
Uncertain	44	46	77	3.7	3.6	3.8	3.6	2.8
No	10	70	70	3.5	3.2	3.9	3.6	2.8
11. Wife's attitude to joint family								
Very desirable	160	24	66	3.8	4.0	4.1	4.0	2.9
Desirable	43	49	72	3.7	3.6	3.6	3.6	2.8
Undesirable	38	58	79	3.8	3.4	3.9	4.0	2.7
12. Wife's expectation of support from children								
Def. or prob. yes	176	30	67	3.9	4.0	4.0	4.0	3.0
Uncertain	36	44	77	3.6	3.4	3.9	3.8	2.4
No	29	48	72	3.6	3.3	3.8	3.9	2.9
13. Family expenditure								
Less than NT $1,000	47	26	64	3.6	3.7	4.1	4.0	2.4
NT $1,000–1,999	114	34	75	3.9	3.7	4.0	3.9	3.1
NT $2,000–2,999	39	41	67	4.0	4.0	4.1	4.0	2.9
NT $3,000 or more	41	37	63	3.7	4.0	3.7	3.9	2.8

TABLE 7 (*Cont.*)

Characteristics of the couple	No. of couples	% who have practiced some form of family planning	% with both husband & wife approving family planning unconditionally	Average number of children wanted by		Average number of children considered ideal for Taiwan		Average number of children born to date of interview
				Wife[a]	Husband[a]	Wife[a]	Husband[a]	
14. Husband's employment status								
Working on farm or business of relative	18	11	72	3.6	4.0	3.9	4.0	3.0
Self-employed	94	27	60	3.7	3.8	4.1	3.9	2.4
Working for someone else	129	43	76	3.7	3.7	3.9	3.9	2.9
15. Wife's farm background								
Some farm exper.	162	31	67	3.8	3.8	4.0	4.0	2.9
No farm experience	79	40	73	3.8	3.7	3.8	3.7	2.8
16. No. of modern consumers' objects[b]								
Less than 4	34	18	50	4.5	4.0	4.4	4.4	3.3
4	30	17	77	3.7	3.9	3.7	4.0	2.8
5	33	21	76	3.6	3.6	4.0	4.0	2.8
6	68	41	69	3.9	3.8	4.1	4.0	3.0
7	47	47	77	3.4	3.5	3.8	3.5	2.6
8 or 9	29	48	66	3.9	4.3	3.8	3.8	2.7

a. In a small number of cases there was not a definite numerical response for these cases, so the averages are based on slightly smaller numbers of cases than are shown in the first column.

b. Based on ownership of following: bicycle, radio, phonograph, electric fan, sewing machine, electric iron, clock, electric pan, newspapers.

On the basis, in part, of these data and surveys, a program has been undertaken in Taichung by the Provincial Health Department to bring family planning information and services to the population. This program continues a smaller and more diffuse program running for several years in other parts of the island and called the Pre-Pregnancy Health Program. The new Taichung program does not aim to persuade anyone to have smaller families. Instead its purpose is to help the large numbers of people who already want to limit family size to do so effectively and safely. This is in many ways different from the task undertaken in many village programs in some countries where the population must first be convinced that they should have smaller families. The Taichung program is unusual in being concentrated in an urban area where the chances for success are greatest because of many favorable factors. For example, it deals with a population that is considerably more literate than the average in developing countries, and the population has more knowledge and more practice in family planning than is usual. The objective is really to help this population to do what it apparently wants to do in such a way as to accelerate the rate of fertility decline. Now, this is a tactical decision of some importance and is quite controversial. Most programs aim at the hardest part of the whole problem and that is to get to the village populations and to persuade people to want fewer children. So far almost all such programs have been failures. It has raised the question as to whether anything could succeed. One of the reasons for choosing the particular program I am describing is to see whether anything can be done where everything is favorable instead of where everything is unfavorable. Dr. Wyon mentioned that 82 per cent of the population of India is in the villages. The other way of saying that, however, is that as many as 18 per cent of those 450,000,000 people are urban and don't live in the villages and that this is a population that is more easily reached and from which influence can diffuse out into the villages. I am not trying to suggest that village programs should be abandoned, I'm simply trying to put this rather different program in its context.

I can only sketch briefly the outlines of this action-study in Taichung.[5] The general objective is to increase the number of families using safe methods to limit family size to the numbers they want. More specific and limited objectives are to test various ways of bringing the message of family planning and the facilities to the public. Specifically, it will test whether it is necessary to contact both husband and wife in a presumably male-dominant culture or whether contacting the wife alone is enough. It will test the efficacy of bringing the message to the public by the written word alone — via the mails. It will also try to establish in a broad way the extent to which the message will diffuse from those who receive it directly to others in the community. What density of effort is necessary for a successful program?

Table 8 shows in outline form the design of the study. The basic unit in the study is the "lin" — this is an administrative unit corresponding to a small neighborhood of about 25 households. The whole of Taichung is divided administratively into about 2,400 such lins. Each lin has been assigned to one of the 12 cells in the study design, and all couples with a wife in the childbearing years in each lin will get as nearly as possible identical treatment. For this purpose the eligible couples are those in which the wife is between 20 and 39 years of age — approximately 36,000.

All the couples will be subject to certain stimuli of a common sort — posters about family planning distributed throughout the city and some material in the newspapers. However, the use of mass media is rather limited.

The rows in Table 8 indicate the basic variations in treatment — the first row is a group of lins which serve as the "control"

[5] For a more complete description of this program, see *Studies in Family Planning,* No. 1, April, 1963 (a publication of the Population Council).

in the experiment. No special treatment is involved there. The second row is a group of lins in which the couples will receive information only by a series of mailings which will include pamphlets and return postcards on which the couple can request a visit by a family planning worker or more written material.

TABLE 8

The "Experimental Design" of the Taichung
Pre-Pregnancy Program

	Number of Lins (Neighborhoods in Each Part of Program)			
		Sectors by Density		
"Treatment"	Heavy	Medium	Light	Total
Nothing	232	243	292	767
Mail only	232	244	292	768
Everything — wives only	232	122	73	427
Everything — wives and husbands only	232	122	73	427
Total lins	928	731	730	2389
Total no. of married women aged 20–39	13,908	11,154	11,326	36,388

The next two rows are those in which the effort is most intensive. The treatment in these two rows is the same except that in one set only the wife is approached and in the other both husband and wife are approached. Of what does "everything" consist? First of all the wife or the wife and husband will be visited in their homes by a trained worker who brings to them the message by the spoken word with the assistance of a variety of visual aids, pamphlets, flipcharts, etc. Secondly, the couples will receive the same mailings as the couples in row two. Finally, the couples will be invited to group meetings of various kinds at which the message will be brought to the group and illustrated with film strips, puppet shows, and group discussions. Wherever possible lin meetings will be held. Also, programs are to be presented at meetings of various organizations: e.g., the farmers' association, home economics classes, occupational associations, etc. Already in the program begun in February, hundreds of such meetings have been held.

The columns in Table 8 represent another dimension of the study design. The city has been divided into 3 pie-shaped sectors approximately equalized initially with respect to socio-economic status and fertility. These sectors vary only in the proportion of their lins which receive the "everything" treatments. The heavy sector has the highest proportion of such lins and the "light" sectors have the lowest proportion. So far as possible, the nature of the "treatment" is exactly the same in lins of each treatment class in differing sectors — "everything" means the same thing in each sector. The point of the variation of density is to see what the effect is on people in "nothing" or "mail only" lins of being surrounded by a higher or lower ratio of "everything" lins. The hypothesis, of course, is that there will be more contagion or diffusion into the nothing lins in the heavy than the light sector.

We expect that the effects of the treatment will be diffuse and will leak over from one cell to another of the design. In this sense, the whole study can be considered to be a single case to be compared with the rest of Taiwan or other large cities. We can examine the trends for Taichung as a whole to see if the action program results in a faster fertility decline in Taichung than elsewhere.

The sample survey of 2,400 couples mentioned earlier is a benchmark of measurements taken before the program began — it includes a variety of measurements of such things as pregnancy and birth rates, attitudes, communication, information and behavior in the field of family planning — along with questions about the social and economic background of the couples. These measurements and others will be repeated in reinterviews of the couples after one year of the program in order to assess changes. The ultimate effect of the program on birth rates in the

TABLE 9

Projections of Taiwan's Population Under Several Assumptions:
Population in 1961: 11,315,000

A. Population by 1986 under several fertility assumptions:
(Mortality is fixed at 1961 levels in each case)

Assumption about Age-specific fertility rates:	*Population by 1986*
1. Stay fixed at 1961 levels.	24,020,000
2. Fertility rates constant at ages under 30 and *no* births after 30	18,617,000
3. Immediate 50% decline in all rates	16,418,000
4. 50% decline in all rates by 1971 then constant	17,590,000

B. Age Distributions

	England & Wales	*Taiwan*	*1986 — Taiwan* *With Immediate 50% fertility decline*	*With no change in fertility*
Age 0–9	15%	33%	21%	31%
10–19	15	20	16	22
20–44	33	34	43	33
45–64	25	11	15	11
65 & over	12	2	5	3
Total	100%	100%	100%	100%

lins of each of the 12 cells of the study design can be assessed by computing fertility rates from the population register for lins falling into each of the treatment sectors.

We aren't sure what effect the program will have, but the measurements being taken will in any case record what happens in Taichung during a period when fertility is likely to fall to some extent irrespective of the formal program. It may well be that we are running along beside the train as it pulls out under its own steam, but at least we will be able to measure the acceleration of the train and to know who the passengers are.

DISCUSSION

Dr. Hisaw opened the meeting for discussion.

JOSEPH SPEIDEL: I am wondering, Dr. Freedman, if there was any governmental subsidy for birth control devices, or how much of some of these peoples' budget this item might be expected to take up.

DR. FREEDMAN: In the particular program that I am describing here the rates are set at a very low level and they are voluntary. That is, anybody who says he can't afford the price can have the contraceptives for nothing. There was quite a discussion at first as to whether the people would value it more if they had to pay for it, but the decision was that the problem of payment should not be an obstacle to acceptance. This program has been going since about the first of February [1963] and it has had very interesting indirect effects which we won't be able to measure for a while but which I think may be very important. For example, the reports are that the price of an illegal abortion has been reduced in some areas as a result of the competition of the availability of materials from this program, and that other kinds of contraceptive services being rendered by private practitioners have come down in price as a consequence. I don't think the economic aspect is important at the moment in this situation.

DR. PARKES: I was very interested in what Dr. Freedman had to say about the desired size of families. That raised in my mind what may be a very difficult question. I nevertheless would like to try it out on Dr. Freedman, if I may. We agree, I take it from the figures I quoted earlier, that the world cannot possibly deal with an increase of 2 per cent per year in the population for very much longer. My question is this: Allowing for unmarried people, sterile couples, and the interval between generations, what size of reared family does 2 per cent increase per annum amount to? In other words is the desire for a family of a particular size, in Taiwan or elsewhere, compatible with knocking down this 2 per cent increase?

DR. FREEDMAN: No, it isn't, but of course they don't have 2 per cent, they have 3 per cent at the moment. One aim is to move from

3 to 2. The implication of your question, however, is quite correct, namely that with families of this size the population will grow very rapidly. As a matter of fact, you will find in the last page [Table 9] of this exhibit some calculations of what the population of Taiwan will be under various fertility assumptions. These were made because some people in Taiwan said that if this program succeeds the population is going to decline and we will be in serious trouble. To meet their fears we made some calculations as to what would happen if there was an immediate decline in fertility by 50 per cent. (We don't anticipate that kind of change in a short run.) The exhibit in Table 9 shows that you have quite a considerable increase in population even with such a decline. To answer your question another way, some calculations for the United States indicate that if we continue with the mortality rates as they are at present, and marriage rates as they are at present, and the people have the number of children that they seem to want and expect in the United States, which is a little over three on the average, that we will have a growth rate that is not very different from what it is at present. It will be about 1.6 per cent which will give us a population of about 350,000,000 by the end of the century. To get to the stationary population situation, family size would have to be cut back by perhaps close to one child, to a little over 2. It depends a little bit upon the marriage situation in the next generation also. For Taiwan this is a one-step matter, that is, this decline would still leave the rate of increase quite high.

DR. PARKES: In my own personal opinion this is a very interesting point as to what rate of increase of overall population can the world be expected to support, and what average size family does that indicate?

DR. FREEDMAN: Much smaller than people say they want in most of these surveys in foreign countries and much smaller than in the United States. People of the United States want 2, 3 or 4 children. That averages out to be a little above 3; that is about what they are having and that accounts for the large population increase.

DR. PARKES: That gives 1.6?

DR. FREEDMAN: About 1.6. It depends. I'd say 1.5 to 1.7.

DR. PARKES: Thank you very much. That is a very interesting figure.

DR. HENRY VAILLANT: Earlier Dr. Hisaw brought up the matter of four generations required for a social revolution. Looking at the graph for the different numbers and the different age groups, I wanted to ask an expert in mathematics how many generations will it take before this large bulge of fertile and prefertile people begins to iron out? It seems to me that it is going to be a vicious circle. You have a high number of people between 0 and 30 years and then they are going to have more children and create a similar population bulge; it is going to flatten out, but how many generations will this require? Even if the average family in Taiwan does have only three children, when will their growth rate begin to fall to the growth rate now in the United States? I don't know whether you have this information or not, but maybe someone else has.

DR. COALE: I think you are exaggerating the difficulty. There is an oscillatory movement in the growth rate before it settles down to a steady state. Let's say that the growth rate settles down if fertility and mortality are stabilized; the growth rates settle down to their long run value in about 30 to 50 years. It doesn't take an indefinite amount of time for it to settle down, rather it does it very quickly.

DR. HISAW: That remark is encouraging.

DR. TIETZE: I think it might be useful if Dr. Freedman would tell this group about the contraceptive methods used in the program now under way in Taiwan.

DR. FREEDMAN: My Chinese friends say that "we use the cafeteria approach." They offer people everything and theoretically that's so. Theoretically the program involves most of the methods that we know about in the West. I say theoretically because there are some practical limitations and there are limitations in what people want. They are told about and have available condoms, foam tablets, diaphragms and jelly, and as of about three weeks ago, a variety of the pill, and they are told about rhythm but that is not anything that interests very many there. They are told about *coitus interruptus*. The method, however, which they are choosing in overwhelming numbers, and I think this is what Dr. Tietze had reference to, is a version of the intrauterine device that has been referred to earlier. This is true in this situation for several reasons. They have quite a long history of the use of an intrauterine device. They have used the Japanese ota ring which involved a considerable dilation and this is what private practitioners very frequently use now. A fair number of the 18 per cent using contraceptives are using that but the new intrauterine device which does not involve dilation is the one which they want. In the meetings, for example, about which I've had reports, the workers say they have had great difficulty in telling about the traditional methods because the people laugh and say, "We don't want that. We want the modern method" and by that they mean the uterine device. I might just comment on this method briefly, since it has not been treated yet. This method is still under study. The intrauterine device is in each case inserted by an obstetrician and the cases are followed by an obstetrician. The device has the great advantage from the point of view of the Taiwanese of being very inexpensive. Once it is inserted it is left in for a year or more and requires no further upkeep or care. It has no association with the sex act itself. It is like the pill in this respect. It has some side effects mainly during the first several months and for perhaps 5 per cent of the women who have an insertion there is a spontaneous ejection. I think I have said enough about the physical character of it. This method is being accepted by quite a large number of people. At the last report I had there were more than 1000 insertions in the city of Taichung since this program began.

HENRY ATKINSON: Coming back again to the subject of family size in the United States, you said that a stationary population would be achieved if the average family size came down — perhaps to 1 or 1.2 children?

DR. FREEDMAN: No, 2.2.

DR. STEVEN PLANK: I would like to have your comments on the relationship between the growth rate and the age at marriage and the time the family size is completed. It seems to me there is a big difference between the habits in the U.S. where the average woman marries and has three children in her early twenties and the situation in Ireland where she would probably not have her children until her middle or late thirties if she got married at all.

DR. FREEDMAN: Yes, of course age of marriage and the proportion married are both very important social variables in many countries.

Some people have advanced a view that it might be desirable to complement family planning programs by trying to initiate social change which will either make marriage later or increase the spacing between children. I don't know that I can say much more about that unless you have a specific question because that is a large area.

DR. PLANK: The question was raised of how many children per family was compatible with such and such a growth rate. It would seem that with the same number of children if you completed your family at the age of 40 instead of at 25 you might cut your growth rate almost in half.

DR. FREEDMAN: Yes, the length of the growth rate depends on the length of the generation and you're saying that if you have a long generation length, that is one way of cutting back on the growth rate and that's certainly true. The figures I was giving you for the United States are based on present age of marriage and present proportions married in the United States. If we had a radical change in our marriage patterns the figures would change, but I don't see any immediate signs of that.

DR. PARKES: The facts that I mentioned include the interval between generations which is substantially the same as the age of child-bearing.

DR. FREEDMAN: Dr. Coale and a colleague have a very interesting article which I commend to you. It deals with this question and shows that the difference, for example, between the Indian pattern and the Chinese pattern in respect to fertility rates and the spacing of children makes a substantial difference in the growth rate even though the size of family is similar. So it doesn't depend only on how many children but it is very important to know how they are spaced.

RONALD L. NUTTALL: You say that 20 per cent of the adult women in the U.S. are sterilized. What are the demographic or social characteristics of these women? Is this a random sample or do they concentrate in certain socio-economic groups or what have you?

DR. FREEDMAN: Well, let me first of all clarify a little bit what I said briefly. Twenty per cent of the couples where the wife is 35 to 39 years old report that either the wife or the husband or both have had an operation which has a sterilizing effect. That includes operations which are done for other purposes. We first asked this question on a national survey in 1955 and we weren't trying to get a prevalence figure and the figures startled us so that in 1960 when the study was repeated by Mr. Whelpton of the Scripps Foundation he asked additionally for the first time whether the operation was contraceptive in intent or whether the sterilization was a by-product of some other therapeutic procedure. The reports, and this is from the patients rather than from the doctors, indicated that about 60% of those were contraceptive. As to their distribution, there are significantly more for Protestants than for Catholics. Now this may be a function of their reporting and an interview, but I don't think so. I think it's very hard for Catholics who go to Catholic hospitals to get the operation. My impression is that this accounts for it. The most important factor is parity; that is, you get a lot more of these operations in the women who have had a lot of children and there is some association with low status. With low status and high parity they are more likely to have the operation. However, it is quite prevalent in all strata of our population.

JOEL B. SHEFFIELD: I am curious about the filtering-out effects that you are investigating in Taichung. Specifically, what is the geographical size of one of these lin units and how are they distributed within the entire city?

DR. FREEDMAN: They vary in size. Two hundred thousand urban people, really urban people, of the three hundred thousand live compactly in a densely settled urban core. Around it there is a very large area. The city is about 15 miles wide at one point, in which there are the farms and you have the hundred thousand farmers. The lins are much bigger out in rural areas. The lin in the city itself is very small because the houses are very densely packed together and the streets in general are narrow.

MR. SHEFFIELD: I suppose this filtering effect would then be a function of the geographical size, the ability to get around conveniently?

DR. FREEDMAN: Yes, I would say that in general there is much opportunity for communication and there is a great deal of communication. There are many markets, many bicycles in the town, people do get around and I think that the opportunities for communication are fairly great. Now we do have questions on that in the base line study. We asked quite a few questions that dealt with whom they talked to, whether they talked to anybody about family planning recently, and whether they know anybody using family planning.

We end up with 55 per cent of the population involved at any given moment being ineligible so that leaves 45 per cent. Of that group there are perhaps half who at that time still don't have the number of children and sons they want. So after all this big canvass you end up with twenty some per cent. I went through this with one of my friends and he said, "If you keep on you will demonstrate that you can't reach anybody." It is something like 21 per cent against which you have to evaluate what you accomplish in a short run. These people become eligible later on in the year.

MR. ROBERT KRETSINGER: During the comments on what the population growth means in terms of family size, I just jotted down a couple of figures here that might be more meaningful. If all the girls that are born reach child-bearing age, if they do bear children, if all of them have a family of three and if the age of the woman is about twenty-five years old when having these three children, that would be about a 2 per cent increase per year, which is pretty disastrous. In a hundred years a population would go from 2 per cent to 10 per cent. And as to the frequency of generations, if she had these children at, say, the average age of 16 or 17 in contrast with the average age of 32 or 34, that would just double the rate. The equation that one would use to get this is just the number of children, say three, divided by 2, that is the mother and father, to an exponential power of one over the number of years, i.e., 1.5 to the .04 power. Now, someone also pointed out that the percentage of women that have children makes quite a difference. If only 75% of the women have children, this would mean multiplying the base by .75, but even with three children and 75 per cent of women bearing children, this is still a positive growth rate, i.e. $(.75 \times \frac{3}{2})^{1/25} = 0.9\%$ annual growth rate.

DR. FREEDMAN: That I think is a fact that most Americans don't realize. I think of the population explosion as an explosion of interest in population. Population has been exploding for a long time, but people are just becoming aware of it. There has been a big increase in interest. I find now that one of the things that shocks middle-class audiences is the negation of their expectation that everything would be solved if only the lower classes would stop reproducing as rapidly as they are. I must admit that it gives me some satisfaction to tell them they are responsible. Only if the great American middle class has fewer children will the rate of population growth go down.

DR. LEVIN: We have talked about the Taiwanese population as though it were a homogenous one or is considered that way. From newspaper and magazine accounts, I have received the definite impression that the refugees from the mainland who came to Taiwan are somewhat different from the natives and that there is some divergence in habits, characteristics and so on. I wonder if this was something that may have been neglected here.

I should also like to comment on this "diffusion" matter. I once had some experience with this. When I was a graduate student in the early days of endocrinology, before the days of grants, graduate students had to work a little harder for their few dollars. One of my first jobs as a graduate assistant was to go into the slums of St. Louis and pick up bottles of pregnancy urine which was collected for us and from which we extracted estrogens. We got the names of the subjects who contributed the urine from the clinics in St. Louis. They were of the lowest economic strata and some of these people were not desirable for our purposes because they showed 4+ Wassermans. For obvious reasons we didn't want to fool with them and so we omitted them. Yet they would find us on the street and would demand to know when we would have *them* collect urine for us. It was apparent that knowledge of the "special" treatment some patients were receiving had "diffused" from subject to subject and those who were being left out felt slighted. So they would seek us out and practically demand that they, too, should be allowed to collect their urine. I think you will encounter a similar experience and will find the subjects coming to you.

DR. FREEDMAN: In answer to your question about homogeneity of the group, you are perfectly correct they were heterogeneous in many respects. I think perhaps the data from that little pilot study shows that in part. The heterogeneity refers to things in addition to the distinction between the mainlanders and the Taiwanese. The mainlanders constitute about 2,000,000 of the 11,000,000 people in Taiwan, and about 9,000,000 are descended mainly from the Chinese who came over in about 1650. In the city in which we are working, however, the proportion of mainlanders is much smaller than that. There is a very heavy concentration of people from the mainland in the capital Taipei, which has about a million people. There is undoubtedly a difference between the mainlanders and the Taiwanese. The mainlanders were likely to have been better educated in the younger generation. That is no longer the case. Actually, the Taiwanese themselves are culturally heterogeneous and came from different parts of the mainland originally and there are differences in dialect at the present time so that our field workers and interviewers for example have to handle several Chinese dialects. Fortunately, the written language is the same.

DR. LEVIN: As far as these studies were concerned, were they considered together?

DR. FREEDMAN: They are considered together because the number of mainlanders is just too few. We did make a separate tabulation. I suppose with the larger study when we get data on the whole sample we will be able to do more with it. I don't think that more than 5–10 per cent of the population of the city of Taichung are mainlanders so that they don't really affect the major problem.

IV

THE ECONOMIC EFFECTS
OF FERTILITY CONTROL
IN UNDERDEVELOPED AREAS

ANSLEY J. COALE, Ph.D.

Chairman: Oscar Harkavy, Ph.D.

DR. HARKAVY *introduced Dr. Ansley Coale as a man responsible for some of the most lucid analysis of population growth and economic development.*

"It is our good fortune," said Dr. Harkavy, "that he has forgone the American Assembly (meeting to discuss United States policy on world population) in order to be with us. Dr. Coale, in addition to being Professor of Economics and Director, Office of Population Research, Princeton University, is currently with the United Nations and is also vice-president of the Population Association of America. He was a member of the National Academy Panel that recently issued a splendid report on the potential contribution of science to world population problems. He is co-author, with Edgar Hoover, of Population Growth and Economic Development in Low Income Countries, *the definitive work to date on this subject."*

THE ECONOMIC EFFECTS
OF FERTILITY CONTROL
IN UNDERDEVELOPED AREAS[1]

ANSLEY J. COALE

Professor of Economics and Director, Office of Population Research, Princeton University.

I AM NEITHER *a sociologist nor a biologist, and I am not a physician. In talking before this audience about the economic implications of population, I am in the position of a young man who was an Army Air Force pilot during World War II. He flew in the early days of the Pacific War one of the first models of air-borne radar, and had some combat experience with this first radar for aircraft. They brought him back to the States and took him before the Army War College, and asked him to give a talk on the tactical uses of air-borne radar. He looked at his audience, which consisted of high-ranking officers, the most junior of whom were one or two majors, but most of whom were colonels and generals. He took a deep breath and said, "There must be dozens of people who know more about the tactical use of air-borne radar than I; however, seeing none of them here . . . . ." That's why I chose to say something on the economics of population. Besides, it is a most serious aspect of*

[1] A fuller statement of the argument contained in this talk was written as part of the background material for a meeting of the American Assembly at Arden House in May, 1963. It will be found in: Philip M. Hauser (Ed.), *The Population Dilemma*. Englewood Cliffs, New Jersey: Prentice-Hall, Inc., 1963.

population today. What I would like to direct your attention to is the relationship between population growth and economic development in the developing areas. I will not discuss the equally interesting problem (though perhaps not as crucial a one) of the same relationship in the industrialized countries.

If one looks at a statistical compendium giving economic facts in the world today, in a year book or popular article, one cannot fail to be struck by the stark contrast between the wealthiest countries and the poorest countries. The countries which have the highest average income — and it is some ten times greater than in the poorest countries — are those which are industrialized, or modernized. And the poorest countries in contrast are those which are characterized by remaining preindustrial, by retaining an emphasis on extractive industries (primarily agriculture), and by the use of traditional techniques of production which have scarcely changed in generations. There is then a contrast, perhaps a growing contrast, between the conspicuous well-being of the modernized countries and the conspicuous poverty of the preindustrial or underdeveloped countries.

Our concern here is the relationship between the demographic features — the characteristics of the population — of these underdeveloped countries and their economic well-being that contrasts so strongly with that of the modernized countries.

There is no need to dwell in detail on the demographic characteristics of the underdeveloped countries. I will mention only the most conspicuous of these.

First of all, every underdeveloped country is characterized by high fertility — by a birth rate of 40 per thousand or higher and by a completed size of family of five or six children or more. In general, this is a fertility which has been sustained at a high level without a perceptible change in the last two or three generations and probably in the remote past as well.

Secondly, the underdeveloped countries are characterized today by low or rapidly falling mortality — by death rates which in some instances are 10 per thousand or lower, by an expectation of life at birth which in some countries has risen to 50 to 60 years. Moreover, in those areas where mortality is not low the typical situation is that it is dropping very rapidly. The reason for this development is in brief that the underdeveloped areas have been able to import from the countries which pioneered in the development of scientific medicine techniques of low cost public health, which even in the absence of substantial social and economic change have been able to bring the major diseases under some measure of control. The use of antibiotics, insecticides and the like and of low-cost sanitation has brought death rates down very rapidly. This has happened repeatedly in areas where there has been no sign of major economic development or industrialization. I am sure most of you are familiar with some of the developments in low cost public health. There are areas (Ceylon is the most often cited) where the death rate has been cut in half in less than a decade. In many instances the expectation of life at birth has risen at least one year per calendar year. That is, the expectation of life may rise from 40 to 50 years in less than a decade.

The consequence of these first two characteristics (of high fertility and low or rapidly declining mortality) is that the underdeveloped areas of the world today are characterized by rapid population growth, or if the growth is only moderate, it tends in general to be rapidly accelerating. Given the technical possibility of reducing the death rate through effective public health techniques and medicine, it seems to me if the death rate is not low there is every prospect that within less than a decade it will be low. Only contact with the rest of the world is essential. In view of the efforts of the World Health Organization, UNICEF, and the private foundations, and of aid programs from the West, it requires only a receptive attitude on the part of the underdeveloped country to enjoy the decline in mortality which is technically feasible today at low cost.

The fourth demographic characteristic of low income countries is a very young age distribution. This is a consequence primarily, in fact almost exclusively, of the high birth rate. Allusion was made in a previous talk to the fact that the age distribution of a population (the proportion in childhood and at other ages) is primarily a consequence of fertility, and depends very little on mortality. It seems a little anomalous that fertility should predominate, but one way of seeing that it is not contrary to common sense is to note that a high birth rate tends automatically to create a large proportion of children in relation to adults. Whether the death rate is low or high, the fertility level determines the rate at which children are introduced into the population relative to adults. Moreover, if high fertility existed in the past, today's parents will be numerous relative to *their* parents, so that the proportion of old people will be small. As mortality rates are reduced, the proportion of children in the population tends to be *increased* slightly rather than the opposite, so that the underdeveloped countries are characterized by very high proportions of children. Typically, 40 to 45 per cent of the population consists of persons under 15, and as mortality has been reduced and is being reduced today, this proportion is rising slightly rather than changing in the opposite direction. All this entails, as we will see later, a high burden of childhood dependency. Relative to the industrialized countries the number of persons in the dependent ages, compared to the number in the productive ages, is much higher. In other words, the burden of dependency is much higher in the underdeveloped countries than in the industrial countries.

The fifth demographic characteristic — density — is not uniform in different underdeveloped areas. Up until now I have mentioned characteristics which are common to almost all preindustrial countries. The density of population in the underdeveloped areas is highly varied. It ranges from less than ten persons per square mile in some of the Latin American countries to over 600 per square mile in Korea. In my remaining remarks I shall discuss the relationship between these demographic characteristics and the process of change from a preindustrial society to an industrialized or modernized society. The process of modernization or industrialization is very complex and involves a gamut of social and economic changes, and that would carry us far beyond what I could hope to cover here if I were to attempt to discuss the relations between population change and this complex process in much detail. What I shall do instead is to present a simplified picture of the process of industrialization concentrating on an essential element to which population has a particularly close relationship. The element on which I will concentrate is the need for capital for the accumulation of productive plants and equipment such as fertilizer plants, transportation networks, and new schools and classrooms. Capital in this sense is an essential component in the complex process of industrialization or modernization. I will emphasize this component more than any other, though I shall mention some others, in discussing the implications of population trends for the prospects of successful industrialization. In trying to characterize successful economic development or modernization I will concentrate on two criteria — again something of an oversimplification. One criterion is increase in per capita income, a very important feature of industrialization; the other is the provision (which I shall emphasize less) of productive employment for the growing labor force in the industrializing countries.

A specific question in which I shall frame this discussion is this: What difference will it make to the process of economic development or modernization if on the one hand the fertility of a country now in a preindustrial phase remains at its present high level, or if on the other hand the fertility is reduced very drastically? The specific form of reduction that I want to discuss

in order to make the argument concrete is a hypothetical reduction of 50 per cent in a period of about twenty-five years. In
other words, we shall try to answer this specific question: How
much difference will it make to the success and to the pace of
economic development if, on the one hand, an underdeveloped
country maintains its fertility unchanged, or if, on the other, it
reduces fertility by 50 per cent in twenty-five years?

This latter hypothetical course of reduction is not without
precedent. There have been a number of areas in the world
where such a reduction has taken place — Japan, for example,
and several European countries. I needn't say that I'm using
fertility in the demographers' sense. I'm not talking about an
impairment of reproductive capacity, but a reduction in the birth
rate.

Before discussing the population implications of these two
alternative courses of fertility, I'd like to say that from an economic point of view it appears possible in the short run, even in
the most impoverished of the preindustrial countries, to keep
up with the growth that would follow from the reduction in mortality that we expect, even if fertility is unchanged. I say this
with the possibility of bringing dismay to some of you who think
that one should present an alarmist picture, saying that if we
don't bring the birth rate down we face inevitable catastrophe
in the underdeveloped areas. I think this view is incorrect in the
short run. India is certainly a major example of a country with
forbidding population prospects. Yet, even in India where if the
birth rate is unchanged in the next generation, the population
would double, approximately, in twenty-five or thirty years,
producing 900,000,000 Indians compared to the approximate
450,000,000 of today — even in that circumstance, there appears to be every technical possibility of somewhat higher per
capita incomes at the end of a generation than today. This is
because the technical possibilities of increasing production by
the importation of more advanced techniques are parallel in a

sense to the possibilities of reducing the death rate by importing techniques in the health field.

The productivity, for example, of Indian agriculture is very low per acre as well as per person. However, by the utilization of further irrigation, double cropping, better seeds, consolidation of land holdings, fertilizer, and without any use of tractors or extensive mechanization of that sort, it appears readily feasible to produce outputs more than twice as great as they are today. Moreover, the likelihood of increases in output in the nonagricultural sectors are even better. Hence, I think it is a mistake in dealing with the short run future to say that if something doesn't happen to the birth rate there is going to be inevitable starvation in the underdeveloped areas. In some instances, perhaps this will happen, but if so I think it would be because of a failure of organization and of the economic development program. I say this, in part because there is widespread misapprehension on this point, but also in part because there is a tendency for people who are preoccupied with the population problem to feel there should be no economic aid unless the recipient countries are prepared to do something about their population. To the contrary, the population problem makes the necessity of economic aid even greater, because of the possibility of keeping up with the rapid population growth of the next generation is a real one only if the economic possibilities are realized, and because a decline of fertility is much more probable in a context of spreading education and social and economic change.

What I want to deal with, then, is not the likelihood that there is going to be disaster, starvation and necessary deterioration in living standards in the short run if fertility is not decreased, but how much difference will it make to the pace and success of economic development if fertility is reduced rather than remaining constant. I want to make the declaration in advance that I don't believe there's any necessary disaster in the next generation if fertility is not changed. But having said something which may sound a little unorthodox, let me emphasize that the goal of merely staying even or perhaps doing only slightly better than today is not a very inspiring goal with annual per capita incomes in India at sixty to eighty dollars. If in the next generation incomes are merely maintained, it would scarcely be a good record and would not do much towards promoting a sense of progress, or social stability or whatever other political purposes economic development might serve. It would certainly be a humanitarian failure of the first magnitude if the miserably low economic conditions that exist in these countries today are not greatly improved.

From a demographic point of view then — let us start with that — from the point of view of population itself, what difference will it make if on the one hand fertility were to be cut in half in an orderly way over a twenty-five year period, or on the other hand fertility were to remain unchanged? It is possible by a standard analytical technique to convert these contrasting assumptions about the future course of fertility into a detailed picture of the development of the size and age structure of the population. I shall summarize some of the salient differences between the two populations. If a million persons at present experience the kind of fertility and mortality conditions that prevail in Mexico or Brazil today, and experience a continuing rise in life expectancy in the future with no change in fertility, in thirty years there would be about 2.7 million people; in sixty years about 8.3 million and in one hundred and fifty years about 245 million people. In other words, if fertility were to be unchanged, reasonable progress in reducing mortality would lead to a multiplication by 245 in 150 years. The implications of a reduction in fertility by 50 per cent would be an increase of population by a factor of two instead of 2.7 in thirty years, by a factor of 3.4 instead of 8.3 in sixty years and by a factor of 10 instead of 245 in one hundred and fifty years. Note that even a reduction of fertility by 50 per cent still provides a great potential for future growth. The startling figures of multiplication by 245 and the like that come from considering the implications of a continuation of current trends, arise in the rather distant future, in the order of hundreds of years from now. It strains our capacity to be concerned about posterity when we worry about events one hundred and fifty years from now. I think most of us are more concerned about the next generation or so, say the next twenty-five or thirty years.

Because of the greater interest of the more immediate future, and because the demographic-economic relations have aspects that differ in the near and more distant future, I shall organize the rest of this discussion around three different time periods: the short run (a period of twenty-five to thirty years or about one generation), a period of medium duration of another generation, or around thirty to sixty years; and the long run from sixty years on out to the indefinite future. One reason for breaking our discussion into these rough time divisions is that during the first generation, the first twenty-five years or so, the entire difference in the population that would result from these two alternative courses of fertility, is concentrated in the child population. Literally, it is concentrated in the population under 25. Obviously, something which affects births in the next twenty-five years cannot affect the number of people who are over 25 at that time. If there is an orderly change in fertility, the difference in number of births at first is not of very large magnitude, so that actually almost all the difference in the alternative populations twenty-five years hence is in the population under 15, the child population. What this means is that we can consider the effect, the demographic effect, of these two alternative trends as being primarily a matter of *age distribution* in the first generation. It is an age distribution effect because the size of the labor force, the size of the adult population, is not affected, only the size of the child population, and therefore the principal social and economic implications arise from change in the shape of the age structure and the reduction of children relative to the adult population.

After a period of twenty-five years or so, an additional implication of these two alternative courses of fertility begins to develop: from then on there appears a difference, at first a growing difference, in the rate of growth of the labor force in the two populations. It is this period (when the difference in growth rate of the labor force first becomes conspicuous) that I wish to consider as intermediate. In the long run the cumulative effect of the difference in rate of growth leads to an ever more important difference in the size of the two populations, and therefore in the density of the population compared to the land or the resources upon which it depends. In sum, we distinguish three periods: a short run period (the first generation) in which differences in dependency appear as the principal effect of different fertility experience; then an intermediate period where added to the difference in dependency is a difference in the rate of growth of the labor force; and finally in the long run, an ever growing and more and more important difference in the density of the labor force relative to resources is added to the age-distribution and rate of growth differences.

Most discussion of "the population problem" is in terms of crowding, or excessive population relative to resources. This turns out to be the most difficult problem to analyze, and the most difficult one on which to reach any certain conclusions. Our frame of analysis will defer the question of density until later, just as significant differences in density result from different courses of fertility only in the rather remote future. We can be much more sure of the economic implications of the age distribution and growth rate differences that differences in fertility imply, and we shall begin with these short run effects.

During this first generation there are only trivial differences in the number of persons of labor force age. In the illustrative numerical projection that I have carried out, at the end of twenty-five years there is only a 4 per cent difference in the number of persons 15 to 64. A strong case can be made that the 4 per cent smaller number of persons 15 to 64 resulting from low fertility does not really mean a lower number of potentially effective participants in economic activity. In the first place, most of these underdeveloped countries are having a great deal of difficulty in providing productive employment for their present labor force, and this difficulty promises to become worse rather than better. Moreover, when there is a reduction of fertility that amounts to 50 per cent at the end of twenty-five years, there is every reason to suppose that the availability of women for employment in the labor force market will be much greater in the population with reduced fertility than with sustained fertility, because there would be 50 per cent fewer pregnant women and 50 per cent fewer dependent children for them to care for. Hence, if additional manpower or womanpower is an economic asset, I think the 4 per cent difference in numbers is more than offset by the much greater availability of women for economic activity that would be the result of reduced fertility. Hence, for twenty-five years the population with reduced fertility would have at least as great a supply of available labor. Obviously, it would have exactly the same resources to work with. I can see no reason to suppose that there will be more minerals or farm land in existence in response to a different number of children. Thus, there is no difference in available labor or resources in the first twenty-five years, but a major difference in that the population with reduced fertility would have many fewer dependents to provide for.

The economy that had those fewer dependents would be in a much stronger position to increase its allocation of resources for productive purposes. It would feel much less pressure to consume everything that it produced each year to provide food and clothing and shelter for its larger and more rapidly growing child population. It would be able to put its efforts into building more factories, roads and the other essentials of development. Here I emphasize again the provision of capital as an essential ingredient of economic development. The economy with reduced fertility would be in a stronger position to provide additional capital, which is certainly a bottleneck item, an essential item with the highest priority in the whole process of development. It would have the same resources and the same labor and would be in a better position to provide capital and would have been in an increasingly better position from the very time that fertility started down.

Over a period of the first generation, the population with reduced fertility because of the age distribution effect, because of the consequent lesser necessity to use almost all of its resources for consumption would be in a stronger position to add to the stock of productive capital that the economy has for development purposes. More than that, whatever resources were made available for enhancing the stock of productive tools and equipment could be utilized in a more immediately productive way if the dependency burden were less. There is less pressure to utilize investable resources for schools, less pressure to put them into housing, when the families are smaller and the school population is growing less rapidly. Capital can be used for factories, irrigation projects, and other purposes that add almost immediately to national product. More immediately productive uses can be made of capital, and more capital can be accumulated. We end up with a paradoxical result. In the first twenty-five or thirty years when one is considering these two alternative population developments, the population with reduced fertility can achieve a faster growth of total national product than can the population with sustained fertility. This is before considering the number of consumers that the national product is going to be divided among. A tangibly greater total national product would be achieved with the same degree of sacrifice of current consumption in order to achieve economic development. The net effect is that on a per capita basis there is a smaller number of consumers and also a greater product to divide among them. So much for the short run.

In the intermediate period we consider a time when the labor force grows more rapidly if fertility is unchanged, and it might appear that some of the advantage that results from reduced fertility would be offset. To the contrary, the implication of a faster growth in the labor force is that in order to keep productivity per worker changing at the same pace or, to take the simplest case, held fixed, one needs to add to the productive equipment, to the stock of useful tools and the like, in a way which is proportionate to the growth of the labor force. In other words, if the labor force is growing 3 per cent a year, one needs, roughly speaking, to add each year 3 per cent to the stock of capital. When the labor force grows more rapidly, in order not to fall behind on per capita output, the pace at which the stock of productive equipment is increased must be stepped up. Meanwhile, the age distribution implications make it more difficult rather than less to do so. We can put this very simply by using a numerical example. If on the one hand you imagine a labor force which is not changing in size and imagine that the economy is investing for nonconsumptive purposes about 9 per cent of its national product, it would add, on the usual economic assumptions, about 3 per cent to the total cumulated stock of tools, so that each worker would every year have 3 per cent more productive equipment to work with. If the population of labor force age were on the other hand growing at 3 per cent (which is about the maximum rate that it is growing in some of the underdeveloped areas today) that same level of annual investment would simply leave the stock of capital per worker unchanged. Actually, a level of 9 per cent is representative of the investment goals in some of the underdeveloped areas today. India, for example, is straining to achieve such a rate of investment. If their labor force were growing at 3 per cent a year that 9 per cent would just enable them to stay even to keep the growth of plant even with the growth of the labor force. Whereas, if the labor force were growing more slowly or in an extreme case not at all, that same level of investment could be used to enrich the endowment that each worker had in productive equipment. After the short run period, in which the age distribution effect dominates, the additional effect of a difference in growth rate is simply to add to the discrepancy in the growth of per capita output and income in the two alternative projections. In the long run this difference in rate of growth has a cumulative effect on difference in size. At first, if we look at the size of labor force alone (and I think it proper to consider this separately because differences in the child population are covered by considering the dependency burden), it is not very different. The first difference we notice in the labor force is a difference in rate of growth, but as time goes on, of course, these different growth rates begin to show up in a substantially different size of the labor force. The size difference reaches a factor of 2 after about seventy years, and then grows cumulatively so that after one hundred fifty years the labor force in a population with sustained fertility would be more than 18 times as big as it would be if the fertility had been reduced.

I said earlier that density is the hardest factor to analyze. I mean one can make a clear economic case for the disadvantages of a higher burden of dependency and for the economic disadvantages of a rapid rate of growth of the labor force. Superficially, density appears to be the simplest element to understand. Overcrowding is easy to visualize, as in the example that continued growth at current rates would produce one person per square foot in six hundred years. However, if you look around the world today, it is not at all clear that within the large range now found, greater density is always an economic handicap. One of the most densely populated areas in the world begins in Boston and extends to Washington, at least. I am not sure that there is any other area in the world of similar extent that has as many people in it. There are 28 million in that 200-mile strip. And it is not at all clear that the density of 2,000 persons per square mile in this region is an economic handicap. Per capita incomes in this part of the United States are higher by 25 per cent than in the rest of the country. I am not at all sure that if the area were less densely settled it would be more prosperous. Now, of course, everyone knows that this area trades with the rest of the country, exporting services and manufactured goods and importing raw materials. But so does Hong Kong. Hong Kong has a density of 13,000 persons per square mile, yet it has raised its annual product by nearly 10 per cent for the last decade. It is able to import raw materials and to export its manufactured services to the rest of the world and to achieve a more rapid economic development than most of the low-income countries which are relatively empty and not densely settled.

Now you might say that Hong Kong is a metropolis which is economically part of China, mainland China, but in fact in the last two or three years only about 16 per cent of Hong Kong's trade has been with China. Most of its trade is on the world market. It is exporting goods to the whole world and importing raw materials from many sources. I do not want to make too much of these examples, but do want to say that in a trading world and in an economy which is not primarily extractive, it is not at all clear what the economic burden of density is.

We can be sure, of course, that for the world as a whole density is an important consideration, and if we imagine the whole world's population getting to be as dense as that of Hong Kong there would be no complementary agricultural areas with which the densely populated area could trade. However, when one looks at an individual country, it is a mistake to consider the implications of population growth wholly in terms of density, or even primarily in terms of density. It nonetheless remains true that if one looks into the far distant future the density implications of the rates of growth in the underdeveloped areas today are literally absurd. Consider Latin America, where the population of Mexico has been growing now at about 3½ per cent a year for the last ten years. Three and a half per cent a year doubles the population every twenty years, doubles it five times in a century, and that means multiplying by 32, and again by 32 in another century or by a thousand in each two hundred years. At this rate in 200 years the population of Mexico would be 35 billion instead of 35 million, and it would be multiplied by a thousand again in the ensuing two hundred years. By such calculations one estimates that in 1200 years or so our descendents would outweigh the earth — a density far beyond any practical consideration. There is no doubt that in the long run with continued rapid growth, density becomes overwhelming. I would like to reiterate, however, that the proper perspective on density as a national problem is probably a long run perspective. In any event the differences in density that would result from these two alternative courses of fertility do not become very pronounced except in the rather distant future — 50 or 60 years away.

We come then to the conclusion, if we examine the implications of these two alternative courses of fertility, that in the short run there is a pronounced advantage which attaches to a reduction in fertility, because it reduces the burden of dependency. In an intermediate period the reduction in fertility would reduce the rate of growth of the labor force and this would have a further economic advantage by making investment more productive of per capita increases in output. In the long run if fertility is not reduced, density reaches absurd levels. At the Office of Population Research we have made some calculations to translate these effects into rough numerical terms. Without describing the techniques of calculation, I shall give you some of the salient results.

We utilized the projected population I have discussed here, and made for each projected population the same assumptions about the factors which determine the growth of output. We calculated the income per consumer that developed for each population projection. I say per consumer instead of per head because in calculating the number of consumers, we counted each child as only a half a person on the grounds that children do not consume as much. This allowance tends to reduce the difference in income between the projected populations. At the end of ten years after the reduction of fertility begins output per consumer is only 3 per cent higher than with fertility unchanged. At the end of twenty years it is 14 per cent higher, and at the end of thirty years, 41 per cent higher. Note that these figures are not the growth in output per consumer, but rather give the output per consumer with reduced fertility relative to what there would be if fertility remained unchanged. In other words, in thirty years there would be 41 per cent higher output per consumer with reduced fertility than if it were unchanged. At the end of sixty years the population with reduced fertility would have doubled the income per consumer, in ninety years three times, and after one hundred fifty years it would have an income per consumer six times as great as the population with unchanged fertility. The economic advantage from reduced fertility in terms of growth in income per consumer is slow at first, but it accumulates to impressive dimensions as time goes by. I should add that these calculations make no allowance for density whatsoever: no allowance for diminishing returns, no allowance for the fact that resources become more expensive and that living space competes with farmland as the population grows. They were made in terms of the effect on investment of differences in dependency and the differential effect of the different rates of growth in the labor force. In one hundred fifty years, leaving out the whole question of diminishing returns and density, the income advantage from reduced fertility reaches a factor of 6, starting with an advantage of about 40 per cent at the end of one generation.

When a country is striving desperately to raise its per capita income from the level of $60 to $80 a year to a more reasonable humane level, a 40 per cent gain is a big one. Also the reduction in fertility makes the increase in the per capita income greater as well as more certain.

I will add only a word about the implication of these alternative future courses of fertility for other aspects of development than the increase in per capita income. Another factor that I want to emphasize especially is that of productive employment for persons of the normal age for economic activity. One of the problems that all underdeveloped countries feel most acutely is the problem of underemployment or unemployment. We have a problem in the United States of unemployment. Five to six per cent of our labor force is unemployed. This problem has been a chronic one, though not as severe since World War II as it was before. Unemployment in the U.S. economy with plants shut down while workers are out of jobs is a matter of simultaneous idle labor and idle capital equipment. It is ordinarily attributed by economists to what we call a "deficiency of effective demand" — the total of the money being spent for consumption, investment and by the government for various purposes is not adequate to utilize our productive resources fully, including the labor force.

In the underdeveloped countries, one also has to deal with something which is called unemployment though to measure it in terms of proportion of the labor force is very difficult. It is more precisely termed underemployment. Most economists feel that the fundamental causes are quite different from the causes of unemployment in the industrialized countries. The difficulty is a lack of adequate organization and of productive equipment to provide work that will produce a reasonable output per worker. The *under*employment usually associated with the underdeveloped economies is the sort of thing one observes in an Indian railway station or in a Mexican barbershop, or in shops in any city in Indonesia, where in the railroad station there are more porters than are needed to carry luggage for any given train, where the barbershop has barbers who are idle most of the day because there are not enough customers, and where a large number of retail shops offer essentially the same merchandise, and the clerks or the proprietors spend most of their day cooling their heels waiting for the few customers to come in. This is called underemployment because in any one of these activities if there were fewer people offering their services the output would not be diminished. This does not show up as the kind of unemployment found in the United States because there is no one actively looking for a job, there being no real job opportunities. This kind of failure to have really useful and productive employment is one of the aspects of extreme poverty in the underdeveloped countries. Even if some of the other aspects of poverty could be alleviated, this is one that also cries for solution. Quite aside from the question of low per capita income, as long as the rapidly growing labor force has job opportunities only of that sort, that is, to show up as additional porters, farm laborers, or barbers when there are already too many, the situation is degrading and undignified and not worthy of a society or economy in the twentieth century.

It is extremely difficult in realistic economic development plans to provide promise of productive employment even for the persons who are now unemployed. When one looks forward to a labor force twice as big thirty years from now, this goal of economic development is seen to be one of the most difficult. During the period when the dependency burden is the principal difference between the two projected populations, the population with reduced fertility has the advantage of more rapid accumulation of capital, which also will make possible a somewhat faster expansion in job opportunities. In the immediate and long run, the slower growth of the labor force will, of course, make the problem of providing productive employment for all a lot nearer to attainment, though I still would not say easy. Add a similar comment about the attainment of other goals such as providing education: universal primary education, secondary education for all within a generation, and growing universities. The difference in costs on the one hand and in the availability of resources on the other is enormous between the population which has a slowly growing child population and the one with the exploding child population that goes with sustained fertility.

In summary, I think there is no need for alarmist statements about how if fertility isn't reduced in the next ten years the population of India or Pakistan will starve, nor for anti-social statements about how if a country is not prepared to accept the advice of Planned Parenthood, we should give it no aid. I think one can in a dispassionate and scientific way see very clearly that the reduction of fertility in the next generation, or as soon as it can be achieved, will be a major element in making possible the modernization and industrialization that every country must pass through in order really to join the twentieth century.

DISCUSSION

Dr. Harkavy asked for questions and comments on Dr. Coale's discussion.

MRS. ALLYN RULE: I do not feel very smug when we talk about "population" and its ensuing problems. I am thinking in terms of our own economy and its birth rate as a problem. I feel that we are now striving to eliminate an increasing rate of unemployment in our own country which is related to our own population increase these past twenty years. I also see that in terms of supply, demand and price policies, our economy has priced itself out of the world market. (This in part due to our high standard of living.) With these aspects in mind, not as an economist, but as an average American, I'd like to ask this question which is pertinent to all concerned about our own economy rather than the economics of the underdeveloped nations: What is the effect of an increasing rate of population increase on a fully developed economy such as our own?

DR. COALE: If you will excuse my disclosing a secret, I had asked Bud Harkavy to ask that very question though perhaps not exactly that way. First, let's get some facts straight about our unemployment and the rise in the birth rate. The products of the rise in birth rate are not for the most part in the labor force yet. If we assume that age 18 is the typical age of entry, the persons entering the labor force this year would have been born in about 1945. The birth rate was up a bit in 1945 over the 1930's, but the really major rise occurred in 1946, 1947 and in the ensuing years. So up until now, certainly during the 1950's, the entries into the labor force were persons born in the 1930's when our birth rate was at a minimum, and below replacement. So that I think the juvenile crime problem and unemployment in the 1950's could scarcely be attributed to the rapid rate of population growth. The children who were being produced in the 1950's and causing our rapid rate of population growth were of preschool age or in school — prelabor force ages. I hate to be negative on this or to give an answer that is contrary to the spirit of your question, but I think in fact that the conservative view — the view of the business community — that the baby boom is good for business is probably a correct one. I would argue that the postwar resurge in the birth rate was probably partly responsible for the fact that our economy in spite of its chronic troubles with unemployment has not had anything like the prewar unemployment problems in the postwar period. In other words, the individual consumer, or rather the individual consuming units in the United States, which do not consist of individuals but of families, have probably been spending a higher proportion of their income on consumption than they would have done if they had smaller numbers of children. Business enterprises in this country have probably been more willing to invest in plant expansion with the prospect of a growing population. The government has also been forced to spend more on schools and highways and other services, so that there has been an upwards pressure on the three principal components of expenditure in this country. Since I think it is generally recognized that our problem of unemployment when it exists results from inadequate "effective demand," and since the baby boom has been a source of increased effective demand, it has probably promoted a higher level of employment, especially since the labor force itself was not growing rapidly during this period because of the entrance into the labor force of persons born during the period of the 1930's. Having said that, I don't mean to give the impression that I would advocate a high rate as a means of stimulating the economy. I think the high rate has been a stimulant to the American economy in contrast to the effect of high fertility in the underdeveloped countries. It has been a stimulant because it is a burden. The individual family has to spend more on consumption, and if you ask the housewife who has three children to care for instead of two, she doesn't look on the necessary extra consumption and spending with any particular pleasure. The same thing would be true of public expenditures on schools and the like. I'll even go further and make a more antisocial economic statement. I think it is also true that the weapons race has been a source of sustained employment in the United States economy. I think the foreign aid program has been, too, to take something which is more humanitarian. I think any burden imposed on the economy tends to be a stimulant to employment, and the baby boom is one of the burdens which has served as such a stimulant. If you are going to ask about the longer range implications, and the whole question of the long range development of the American economy, the problem is more complex. While it has been a stimulant, the burden has been nonnegligible in some of its social costs. The number of children added to the U.S. population between 1950 and 1960 was greater than the addition between 1900 and 1950. We had a fantastic explosion in the child population because we had high fertility after a period of very low fertility. The school age population did not increase at all between 1930 and 1950, then it increased by about 52 per cent in one decade, and we had the doubling-up in the schools, two shifts going to schools, and shortages of school rooms, shortages of teachers and so on. You must not exaggerate this as far as present implications are concerned, because we are now through the most striking growth of the child population. That is, the burst of primary school age population is past and the wave front, the very rapidly growing part of child population in the United States, is now in secondary schools. Any secondary school teacher can recognize it, it's the tenth grade that is the big problem right now, and then it will be the eleventh and twelfth. Then the first of the baby boom hits the colleges about 1965. If the college age people here think it was hard for them to get into college, wait until the kids born in 1947 come along. The births in 1947 were 33 per cent more numerous than they were two years before that. We are going to see a tremendous wave coming into college and the admission standards are going up much higher. During the 1960's we are going to have to face the educational consequences at the college level which have already been faced at the primary school and now are being faced at the secondary school level. We are also going to have to face an increased wave of admissions into the labor force and provide jobs at the same time that automation is coming along. So actually I think that up until now probably the demographic development since the war has been favorable to employment. The crucial employment problems we haven't yet met and we will have some. I probably gave you more of an answer than you wanted.

MRS. RULE: No, you haven't really answered me because I think you haven't stated the problem in terms of the capital that will be necessary to employ this population when they are either out of high school or college. What is the problem for our own society in terms of our so-called "stagnating economy"?

DR. COALE: Well, if we need more capital that would keep the economy from stagnating.

MRS. RULE: But do we have this capital potentially available, or, to put it another way, at present are we putting the capital "in" that will provide for these groups?

DR. COALE: We are providing some of the needed capital, and have the capacity to provide much more. We have the schools now. We are perking along at only about 60 per cent of capacity in the steel mills, and steel is the principal source of capital goods. We have a lot of excess capacity in our capital goods industries. What I am worried about is that although we have the capacity, we won't provide the capital for the jobs; I don't think you can make a strong case that the United States is heading for impoverishment because of its population growth, and I would say that if we end up with 350 million people at the end of the century (which is the biggest number anyone has suggested) that there is every reason to suppose that the per capita income (after adjustment for inflation) will be substantially higher than today. We would still be below the density of most of Europe, which is thriving. The problem is that our *economy* is not growing rapidly enough. Our economic growth is slow, although we have ample means in technique and in capacity and capital goods industries and in the steel and other basic industries to match the growth of our labor force several times over. What I am afraid of is when this sharp burst appears on the labor force in the middle '60's at the same time that we are introducing capital in forms that are labor saving that there will be a tendency for rising unemployment and it will create all kinds of social problems. It may make juvenile delinquency worse. One of the things it might do, incidentally, is postpone marriage and lead to a reduction in the birth rate, because one of the reasons that youngsters have been getting married at decreasing ages during the '50's is because those who were born in the 1930's represent a permanently small group — a real advantage for them. There's no way of enlarging them — if they weren't born at that time, there's no other way of getting more people at that age today. If a small number of people were born in 1935, (how old would they be today, 28?) there is no way of getting more 28-year olds today. When they graduated from college there was a tremendous shortage of young entrants into the labor force, and they were getting $6,000 a year beginning jobs. There was a cartoon of a young kid saying to GE, "Don't call me, I'll call you!" And when they get to be junior executives, there's going to be a shortage of junior executives, and when they get to be 65 their companies will be pleading with them not to retire.

MRS. RULE: I have another question. How can we relate our own economic problems concerned with our own population birth rate in relationship to the use of our own capital and its effect on the available capital for the underdeveloped countries? If we don't have extra capital, where will the underdeveloped countries find the capital that is needed to support their increasing populations? Even granting that they can decrease their present birth rates, where will they find capital?

DR. COALE: I certainly agree this is a problem. Again, I don't think our population is a major part of this. I would worry more about Congress than I would about the birth rate, and in fact we have been putting too much of our aid for my taste in military form rather than in general support. It is extremely difficult, incidentally, to make effective use of aid. It isn't true that if we had more dollars available they would always be helpful because it is very hard to turn dollar aid into a productive gain. But again, I wouldn't think that our own population development is going to be a major factor in this. One last point on the U.S. There is a widespread false belief that the birth rate in the United States is something which would be affected very much by a stepped-up Planned Parenthood Campaign, by opening more birth control clinics in the slums of the United States and preventing the unwanted children that under-privileged people have. The reason I think that is based on a mis-understanding is that our birth rate was just about at the replacement level in the 1930's and no one who has given any consideration to this problem thinks we have forgotten how to use contraceptives since then. To the contrary, the knowledge of and the effective use of contraception is much more widespread today than it was in the 1930's, and the reason that we had our postwar baby boom was not because suddenly we had more ignorant people who didn't know about birth control. The reason that our birth rate is so high in the United States is because middle class people want larger families. The model size of family desired is 2, 3, and 4, and this size leads to our current population growth. Ninety per cent of white American couples where the wife is over 30 and does not suffer from some fecundity impairments, use some form of birth control. I don't mean to deny there is a Negro problem or a general minority group problem in regard to lack of access to birth control measures, but that 90 per cent account for the vast majority of our births. If you were to make contraceptive knowledge available to the other 10 per cent and to the 11 or 12 per cent of population that is nonwhite, it wouldn't make a large dent in the birth rate. The high birth rate in the United States is due to people who by and large can afford children and decide to have them. It is due more especially to the fact that we no longer have people who don't get married, and we have almost no childless couples. In fact, the decline in the proportion of childless couples has gone so far that the medical profession has had to reassess its judgment as to the proportion who are sterile. The proportion of one-child families has gone down. What's happened is a disappearance of spinsterhood, childlessness, and the one-child family, and a settlement on a consensus of 2, 3, or 4.

DR. STEPHEN PLANK: I have three questions, unrelated. First, what do you see as the economic determinants and consequences of the 5 per cent drop that apparently has taken place between January '62 and January '63 in the United States fertility rate? Number 2 is a comment — you mentioned Hong Kong and its population density, which you seem to imply was acceptable. In a recent World Health publication they talked about what was necessary to get an apartment in Hong Kong. It was necessary to have five adult occupants, and the apartments are only 10 feet by 12 feet. This isn't really acceptable, I feel. Thirdly, and more importantly, on your curves for the growth of the Indian economy and your statement that they can without too much difficulty maintain the status quo, I have the impression that over the last 35 years India has gone from an agricultural economy with an export of grain to an agricultural economy which has to import a lot of grain. Also that the caloric intake and so forth has shown a steady decline. What warranty is there for the optimistic view that they can even maintain the status quo? With increasing population the pressure is on marginal resources so that it may cost more and more in capital to get less and less in return.

DR. COALE: Let's see if I can reconstruct the first question. Your question was about the decline in fertility in the United States. It was about 5 per cent in the last year. Actually, it has been going down somewhat irregularly since 1957. In cohort terms, the most recent group to be interviewed in the GAF Study conducted by Michigan and the Scripps Foundation, the 20 to 24 year olds in 1960 gave answers showing that this youngest group is expecting a smaller family than their predecessors, five years older. I can't pretend to account for it; I don't understand why the birth rate went up so; I am not in a position to say why it is apparently going down. Except that as a general social statement, I would say that as soon as the demographers are convinced that the postwar baby boom is not temporary, then it is going to turn out to be so. Our predictions have been uniformly wrong and our explanations probably not much better. On the Indian problem, I've seen these figures that show a steady downward trend in consumption for the past 30 years. The lack of development in the Indian economy is probably genuine from late in the nineteenth century until 1940 or so, and you can if you choose blame this on the colonial English government. That may not be fair. I think the idea that any government had any responsibility for economic development, whether it was a colonial one or local one, is pretty much of a mid-twentieth century idea. In fact, economic development as a sustained effort is new in India. Whether the English would have done it had they stayed, I can't say. The Indian government certainly has. The crop yields and so on are not too reliable if we go back in the records, but from '51 to '61 agricultural output has grown at a substantially greater rate than the population has. The rest of the economy is growing still more rapidly. The rates of increase have been in the order of 3.7 per cent a year or something like that compared to about 2 per cent for the population. This has been true in every economy that has made any serious development effort.

If you are going to ask me if Hong Kong is overcrowded, of course it is. And I didn't mean to say that the overcrowding in housing isn't a tragedy and causing a lot of human suffering. So is it in Mexico City, and in Rio De Janeiro. They are just about as overcrowded. This is a matter of inadequate housing and let me say that they have improved their housing more rapidly in Hong Kong than in Brazil during this period in spite of the fact that if they get more land they have to dig it up out of the harbor and deposit it. What I am saying is that they have increased their per capita output, they have nearly doubled it in ten years, and Hong Kong is now in the top twenty of the countries in the world in the volume of trade — it surpasses Belgium in world trade. The Japanese are complaining about the competition in plastics, textiles and so on from Hong Kong. It is a resounding economic success. All that I am saying is in spite of the fact that they have a density of 13,000, it just isn't an overwhelming barrier to their successful development.

DR. VENNING: I would like to comment on what I believe is an unjustified complacency about the short term view in relation to some of these countries in the East. I would like to ask one or two questions. First of all, I would like to know what the capital development in India is in fact. Secondly, I would like to ask what is the rate of growth of the national product in Ceylon at the present time. I think the last speaker's calculations were based on certain assumptions of optimum growth and efficiency; that everything might not be disastrous if there were efficient spread of ideas, agriculture, *et cetera, et cetera*. Now, I don't believe these things are as easy as that and I would be interested if you would make some calculations as to what the effects would be if you have no population control over a short term and on the assumption that there's not going to be an increase in the gross national product. In a place like Ceylon, for instance, the total amount of goods available will stay the same while the population is growing. It would not be going upwards.

DR. COALE: You can assume any problem you like. I wouldn't argue that Ceylon is developing successfully. I said countries that have made a serious effort in economic development and I am not sure of Ceylon's. As far as India is concerned, the calculations that I made for India were based on several years of research and on interviews with more than a hundred economists, and the Planning Commission. Our assumptions were more conservative than theirs in every regard in respect to the expansion of agricultural output and in regard to the capital output ratio, and in fact almost every economic index you want to name. I think that probably the Indian development program is rather inefficiently run and actually if you were to assume that Indian agriculture was going to be efficient like Japanese agriculture I would be talking about 3 or 4 times the output, not twice. Our calculations are based on the plans of the Indian Agriculture Ministry, and really do not represent any more rapid growth in output in agriculture or any other sector than they have been achieving. India's performance is short of the targets, but our calculations were really not very extreme in that connection. Actually, in the last decade they have kept ahead of their population growth. Now, perhaps Ceylon hasn't. Ceylon remains sort of a plantation economy trying to export a few crops in the world market with prices that are uncertain and they've never had a very thorough development program. There are other countries that haven't either, and of course it is true that rapid population growth is a handicap under those and other circumstances, and if you want to assume that output is going to stagnate you will, of course, get per capita output going down just as rapidly as the population grows. I think that prospect as a general proposition for under-developed countries is not realistic. I think most of the under-developed countries, assuming that they can overcome their political difficulties and get any kind of assistance, will not be so affected. If they can't do that, they certainly aren't going to have a birth control program that works.

DR. TIETZE: May I draw your attention to an apparent paradox: there are a number of countries in South America and Africa, where I believe one could make a good case that they would be better off if they had 2, 3 or 4 times the population they have now. On the other hand, one can make an equally strong or even stronger argument that they would be a good deal better off if their rate of growth were one half, one third, or one fourth of what it is now. I have found it exceedingly difficult to explain this paradox and to achieve some kind of synthesis. I wonder whether you can help me find a formula.

DR. COALE: I hope I can. In the first place, I'm not so sure of the facts. If you take Brazil, which is cited as a big empty country, it has 70 million people (rather 71 million and the 1960 census was a big surprise) and the population is growing at 3.6 per cent per year. They will have 140 million, at this rate, in twenty years. There are people who study this sort of question who are quite uncertain that the whole Amazon will ever support anything substantial in agriculture. If you clear out the jungle, the rainfall leaches out the soil, so that some of the emptiness of the Latin American countries may be an illusion. The belief that these countries need population is based on what I'm beginning to believe is the density illusion. It may be true, and I'm not sure it is, that they have very low density relative to their resources. The point is that all underdeveloped countries have in common a very uneconomically high density *relative to their capital*. They all have too high a ratio of population to their capital equipment. That can always be remedied because capital can be created. But to create more capital is a matter that takes time, and so the question is the growth of the capital stock versus the growth of the population. If you suffer from an excessive density of population relative to capital, and I think all underdeveloped countries do, then a rapid rate of population growth makes it impossible to repair that situation; a slow growth rate makes it possible. So that if you want to turn it around and raise the question of *density relative to capital*, you may be able to clarify this question.

DR. SEYMOUR GRAY: You have touched upon one parameter in the development which perhaps deserves more amplification. It is the eradication of disease, and its effect upon economics. It has been well demonstrated that in those countries where malaria and trachoma and other diseases which afflict some two-thirds of the population have been eradicated, the gross national product and the per capita income have risen considerably. Now the question is, are we on the horns of a dilemma? If we decrease our infant mortality and prolong life expectancy, are we by so doing going to increase the population further? Or are we, by improving the health of the developing countries, improving their economy so that they have better education? And, as a result of better education and a higher level of development, the population problem will take care of itself on that basis alone. How do you compromise the triad of economics, of eradication of disease and population problems?

DR. COALE: I am glad this question has come up because it is one that bothers public health people a great deal. And you raise a lot of complex issues. Let me take your point about the implications for the growth of population and remind you of Ron Freedman's discussion earlier in which he said in the value system of the Chinese, at least, it is a lot easier to introduce fertility control when all the children are surviving than when they have to maintain high fertility in order to insure their survival, so that I am not sure the proposition will stand historical scrutiny in all parts of the world. It is quite likely in most parts of the world that there is no hope of bringing the birth rate down until you have first brought the death rate down. Secondly, I think that the question you raise is a genuine source of concern in setting a background. The problem we have to work on is not one as far as any genuine policy decisions are involved. I think the medical profession unnecessarily feels guilty about having brought the death rate down; it might feel guilty about not having done enough about the birth rate. But there isn't a choice. I can't imagine a government that is going to say we could eradicate malaria in this country with means that are well within our resources but we are not going to. I can't imagine the medical administration that would go along with that as long as the technical possibility is there. As a friend of mine once said, it is always the parents whose babies are not dying who would make that choice. And as a goal in itself, as a humane goal of reducing suffering and premature sorrow and what have you, I think one has to be in favor of disease eradication. It simply makes it more essential that something be done about fertility. However, it is also true that greater productivity may help offset some of the problems and give us a breathing spell in which to work on the fertility problem.

V

FRONTIERS IN METHODS
OF FERTILITY CONTROL

Frontiers in Methods of Fertility Control
GREGORY PINCUS, SC.D.

The Inhibitory Aspects on Gonads of the Male
WARREN O. NELSON, PH.D.

Possible Easy Methods of the Future
JOHN ROCK, M.D.

Some Facts About Legal Abortion
CHRISTOPHER TIETZE, M.D.

Discussants:
  A. S. Parkes, F.R.S., Ph.D., D.Sc.
  C. R. García, M.D.

Chairman: Roy O. Greep, Ph.D.

DR. GREEP *explained that the panel discussion, which made up Session V, had been devised to present a variety of approaches to the matter of fertility control. The Chairman introduced the speakers and discussants at the beginning of the Session, and then presented the speakers individually in turn.*

In presenting Dr. Gregory Pincus, the first speaker, he told of the importance of his research and said that "the pioneering work of Dr. Pincus on the orally active contraceptives has unequivocally demonstrated their effectiveness." In introducing

Dr. Warren Nelson, he referred to him as a "partisan of the male gonad, while Dr. Pincus was a partisan of the female gonad."

When introducing the third speaker of the panel Dean Greep pointed out that the meeting had already had a "presentation on the female and one on the male, and we have pretty well exhausted the sexes. This might pose a problem to some people but not to the virtuoso who is the next speaker, Dr. John Rock." In presenting the final speaker, Dr. Greep's comments were to the effect that "it is one thing to prevent conception and another to cancel the pregnancy after conception has occurred. Dr. Christopher Tietze is a world authority on the practice of legal abortion."

FRONTIERS IN METHODS

OF FERTILITY CONTROL

GREGORY PINCUS

Research Director, Worcester Foundation for Experimental Biology; Research Professor, Boston University Graduate School.

IN ATTEMPTING to discuss frontiers in systems of fertility control, I have decided to confine myself to the more popular member of the species, namely the female. Again, at risk of appearing to be theoretical I should like to review very briefly in the course of the discussion certain basic phenomena which must be considered in the development of any method in which the female is the primary controller of fertility. Therefore, I will in part expatiate somewhat on a few things that Dr. Parkes (1) has presented and also will touch on some of the matters covered by Dr. García (2).[1]

To get into the subject matter at once, let us recall that from the point of view of the organization of reproductive processes in the female there are really two major steps: one is the production of the gamete, the egg, and the other is its fertilization and eventual birth. In other words, fertilization or pregnancy preceded by ovulation is shown diagrammatically in Figure 1. The system has been described by Dr. Parkes (1) and I shall briefly recall it to you. It is the system in which a hypothalamic neurohumor stimulates the adenohypophysis, i.e. the anterior pituitary,

[1] Numbered references are on page 203.

to produce two types of gonadotropin, FSH and LH. LH is primarily responsible for the preovulatory swelling and rupture of the follicle, FSH for the growth of the follicle previous to ovulation, and both are responsible for the production of estrogen and progestin which operate in a negative feedback system that has been described to you.

As we can see from Table I there are really involved in this system four loci which are essential for the sequence of events

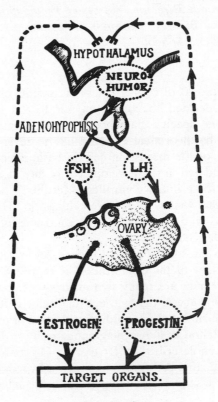

FIGURE 1

leading to ovulation. What I want to talk about initially are the attacks which are being made on each of these four loci. The first is the hypothalamus itself which produces the LH stimulating neurohumor, the ovulation stimulator; the second, of course, is the anterior pituitary which receives the neurohumor and responds by releasing LH; the third is the blood which carries the LH secreted by the pituitary to the ovaries; and the last is the ovarian follicle itself which is the receptor organ.

TABLE I

Loci Essential for the Sequence of Processes Leading to Ovulation

LOCUS	FUNCTION
Hypothalamus	Production of LH-Stimulating Neurohumor
Anterior Pituitary	Receipt of and Response to Hypothalamic Neurohumor
Blood	Carrier of LH Secreted by the Pituitary
Ovarian Follicle	Swelling and Rupture in Response to Increased LH

I would like to discuss with you the question, what do we have available in terms of frontiers, things to be done, in each of these four loci? First of all, as far as the hypothalamus is concerned there are at least two broad types of agents that have been used to act upon it, ordinarily to inhibit it from producing its neurohumor. The first of these are the series of CNS active drugs, central nervous depressants for the most part, and the second are the steroids.

In Table II are the lists of some of the pharmacological agents used in blocking of ovulation by inhibiting the hypothalamic mechanism. You can see that there is quite a list here, anti-adrenergics, anticholinergics, ataractics, anesthetics, and barbiturates. All of these central nervous system depressants (if you want to call them that) have been shown to inhibit ovulation in experimental animals. Their application to the human has been, shall I say, at most incidental; there have been occasional and not very meaningful reports of sterility due to the use of one or another of these drugs. The amounts that appear to be necessary for use, practical use, appear to be rather large and probably are contra-indicated. I'll return to the consideration of one of these drugs in a little while.

TABLE II

Pharmacological Agents and Blockade of Ovulation

Antiadrenergics	Ataractics	Barbiturates
Dibenamine	Chlorpromazine	Nembutal
SKF-501	Reserpine	Dial
Anticholinergics	Anesthetics	Ipral
Atropine	Morphine	Amytal
Banthine	Ether	Barbital
		Phenobarbital
		Prominal

In Table III we list the agents that have been indicated as possible inactivators of circulating gonadotrophin; this now is essentially the blood LH. You see that there have been factors obtained from plants, the lithospermum factor, the Lycopus factor, the enzyme lysozyme from animal sources which appears to destroy gonadotropin. Then there are certain antigonadotropins that have been extracted along with the gonadotropins

TABLE III

Inactivators of Circulating Gonadotropin

SOURCE	ACTION
A plant — Lithospermum ruderale	Enzymatic Destruction?
A plant — Lycopus virginicus	Enzymatic Destruction?
Animal — Lysozyme	Enaymatic Destruction
Animal — Pituitary	Antigonadotropin — perhaps competitive inhibitor
Animal — Fetal Serum	" "
Animal — Human Urine	" " — against HCG*
Animal — LH Antibody	LH-Binding

* HCG = Human Chorionic Gonadotrophin

themselves from the pituitary. Nobody knows their chemical nature; they have been indicated only on the basis of biological activity in the sense that as you purify pituitary gonadotropins you have evidence that you get rid of some of these inhibitors. There is a factor reported present in serum which appears to be very active. Its chemistry is unknown. The factor in human urine which has been reported in recent years and has been worked on fairly intensively in the last two years appears to be a consistent inactivator of gonadotropin, chiefly chorionic gonadotropin (3). Finally, the development of an antibody to LH to which Dr. Parkes referred is something still very much a matter for study in the laboratories, so I think we will hear more about this later.

To my surprise, I have found little evidence of anything which really acts directly upon the pituitary. All the so-called pituitary inhibitors, as far as I can see, appear to act through the hypothalamic mechanism. So I have nothing to tell you about substances that act directly upon the pituitary. This, I must say, is rather curious, and those of you who are interested in research problems should find a nice one here, because the pituitary is in fact a very active gland, and there should be very many agents which should act upon it directly. With the exception of a possible testosterone influence on pituitary FSH secretion (4), I know of no evidence of any, shall I say, obviously effective agents acting on the pituitary itself.

For agents that act directly on the ovaries, we have a situation which is a little anomalous. It's anomalous to me because the experimental data with which I am acquainted suggest relationships not easy to understand. The method that we have used for studying substances which might act directly on the ovarian follicle is a method which, when we first started, seemed experimentally sound. It involved inducing ovulation in immature animals by the administration of exogenous gonadotropins and looking for inhibitors of such induced ovulation. We used a very familiar procedure: as an FSH we used pregnant mare serum and followed it by HCG as an LH. In other words, we primed the animal with pregnant mare serum (PMS), stimulating follicle growth, then gave human chorionic gonadotrophin (HCG) to cause ovulation. In fact we caused superovulation by our optimal regime. Then at some critical time in this ovulation stimulating regime we administered presumed antagonists to the ovulation process, and assumed that these antagonists act on the follicle to inhibit it from rupturing.

In Table IV is a list of compounds that Purshottam, Mason and I (5) studied in the mouse receiving superovulating doses of PMS and HCG. You see that the list includes the so-called CNS active substances. The reason why we used these was because previously, in intact adult animals, these substances had been shown to be ovulation inhibitors (see Table II), but presumably by acting at the hypothalamic level. Nonetheless when we gave these same substances to superovulated animals in which, as it were, we obviated the hypothalamus, many of them were clearly inhibitors of superovulation. Chlorpromazine is quite active, probably significantly active at least at 0.01 milligram per mouse. Reserpine, which is the most active of them, is not on this list, and it is active again at about the same level or a little less. The others are active at various dosage levels, and for the most part we attained complete inhibition of superovulation with the use of a variety of these ataractic and CNS depressant agents. This surprised us very much. It was our expectation that we might find quite a different type of substance. In an extension of these studies Dr. Purshottam has found other tranquilizers effective in mice (6).

Among a number of steroids tested we also found inhibitors (Table V). Progesterone at 0.5 milligram per mouse completely inhibited superovulation. The other steroids were marginally effective. 17-ethynylestradiol-3-methyl ether, which forms part of practically all of the oral ovulation inhibitors now used as

TABLE IV

Compound	No. animals in test	Dosage per animal (mg.)	% of animals ovulating	Mean no. of eggs ovulated	Inhibition of ovulation*
Equanil	30	0.3	60	7.0	+
		3.0	20	0.8	++
		5.0	0	0	+++
Sparine	20	0.1	60	11.8	+
		0.5	0	0	+++
Chlorpromazine	30	0.01	60	6.4	+
		0.125	20	2.2	++
		0.25	0	0	+++
Atarax	20	0.1	80	14.6	
		1.0	20	4.0	++
Trilafon	20	0.01	100	22.8	
		0.1	0	0	+++
Paxitol	20	0.1	80	17.6	
		1.0	0	0	+++
Compazine	20	0.1	60	11.0	+
		1.0	0	0	+++
Stelazine	20	0.02	80	21.8	
		0.20	20	2.4	++
Atropine	10	0.04	60	5.4	+
		0.4	0	0	+++
Metropine	10	0.25	80	14.0	
		0.5	40	3.6	+
Demerol	10	0.02	100	25.4	
		0.2	60	13.8	
Phenobarbital	10	0.10	60	17.6	
		1.0	40	6.0	+
Dibenamine	10	0.05	80	8.2	+
		0.5	20	1.4	++
Benadryl	10	0.10	60	16.8	
		0.5	60	6.8	+

* + indicates significant reduction in number of eggs; ++, significant reduction in both ovulation rate and number of eggs; and +++, complete suppression of ovulation.

oral contraceptives, was marginally active at 50 micrograms in the mouse, estrone at about a milligram. You will notice that the doses of the steroids necessary by and large are fairly high compared to the CNS depressants of Table IV. Actually this problem has been pursued a little further in our laboratory. I'll try to give you some recent data.

We have used reserpine as the agent which was the most effective in the mouse, and have tried it in the rat on the grounds that maybe the mouse is a particularly susceptible species, but we find that the rat is just as susceptible (7). In Table VI are

TABLE V

The Effect on Ovulation of Various Compounds Administered on Day 23 to Immature Mice Subjected to the Standard Ovulating Procedure

Compound	No. animals in test	Dosage per animal (mg.)	% of animals ovulating	Mean no. of eggs ovulated	Inhibition of ovulation*
Estrone	10	0.10	100	20.8	
		1.0	80	7.8	+
17-α-ethinyl estradiol 3-ME	10	0.01	80	15.4	
		0.05	80	7.8	+
Cortisone	10	0.3	80	12.2	
		3.0	40	4.8	+
Progesterone	10	0.25	60	5.8	+
		0.5	0	0	+++
17-α-ethyl-19-nor testosterone	10	0.10	100	22.6	
		0.50	80	17.2	
17-α-ethynyl estra-10-enelone	10	0.15	50	11.6	
		1.50	10	1.6	++
17-α-methallyl 19-nor-testosterone	10	0.10	100	19.2	
		1.50	80	4.0	+
6-α-chloro-11-acetoxy progesterone	10	0.50	100	17.8	
		2.0	40	5.2	+

* + indicates significant reduction in number of eggs; ++, significant reduction in both ovulation rate and number of eggs; and +++, complete suppression of ovulation.

TABLE VI

Effects of Reserpine (Constant Dose) on Ovulation in Intact Rats
(Given at Various Times between PMS & HCG)

TREATMENT	No. Rats	No. Ovulating	Average No. Ova per Rat $\pm$ S E
PMS-HCG Controls	5	5	58.0 $\pm$ 8.2
125 μg RESERPINE			
54 hrs. before HCG	10	10	54.0 $\pm$ 8.1
32 hrs. before HCG	9	9	56.4 $\pm$ 7.8
7 hrs. before HCG	9	9	21.0 $\pm$ 0.4
1 min. before HCG	6	6	56.2 $\pm$ 9.3

data on reserpine given to intact superovulated immature rats.
Note that the average number of eggs per rat is 58. (This is
indeed superovulation!) If the reserpine is given at certain intervals before the ovulating injection of HCG, there is no effect.
At 54 hours before HCG, which is when the PMS is given, at
32 hours before, no effect, but at 7 hours before you see a
significant reduction in the number of eggs ovulated. Again,
reserpine given at one minute before HCG no longer acts as an
inhibitor. Thus, there is a critical time at which reserpine given
to a rat will inhibit ovulation. Now, you may say maybe the
animal's own pituitary or hypothalamus is contributing something to this in spite of our feeling that we may be obviating
these by the use of exogenous gonadotrophin. So we have gone
to the use of the hypophysectomized rat, thus completely removing its own pituitary. The data of Table VII demonstrate that in
the hypophysectomized animal, using the same superovulating
regime, but giving the reserpine just at the same time that the
HCG is given, you can with 25 micrograms essentially reduce
the superovulation to significantly lower levels, and with 50
micrograms get down to a very small amount of ovulation in a
few animals. Thus, reserpine appears to act to prevent ovulation
at the level of the follicle. How it does this is a problem which
we propose to examine further.

TABLE VII

Effects of Reserpine on Ovulation in Hypophysectomized Rats
(Reserpine Given Approximately 1 Minute before HCG)

TREATMENT	No. Rats	No. Ovulating	Average No. Ova per Rat $\pm SE$
PMS-HCG Controls	37	37	39.7 ± 2.1
10 μg Reserpine	11	11	37.5 ± 4.3
25 μg Reserpine	9	3	1.9 ± 0.17
50 μg Reserpine	36	6	0.30 ± 0.01

Actually, of course, for practical ovulation inhibition we now use steroids, and particularly the progestin-estrogen combination described by Dr. García which has proven much the most effective. Literally hundreds of steroids have been tested as ovulation inhibitors in several types of test animals. The one most commonly used is the rabbit because it is an animal which ovulates only after mating, at about 10 hours after mating, and by preceding the mating with the administration of an inhibitor one may prevent this ovulation. In Figure 2 are four of the 19-norsteroids which have proven effective both in laboratory tests and in field trials as contraceptives. Norethynodrel in combination with estrogen is called Enovid, norethisterone in combination with estrogen is called Orthonovum, the acetate of norethisterone called Norlutate is sold in combination with an estrogen as Anovlar outside the United States. Ethynodiol diacetate is a compound which Dr. García, Dr. Paniagua, Dr. Shepard and I have done some field work with, particularly in Puerto Rico (8). Again, combined with estrogen it is an extremely potent compound. These are the types of substances which are really extremely effective and in very low dose in the human. As a matter of fact, the contraceptive dosages that can be used are of the order of magnitude of those shown to be inhibitory in the rat and the mouse. In other words, the human dose is extremely low.

PROGESTINS TESTED AS ORAL CONTRACEPTIVES IN FIELD TRIALS

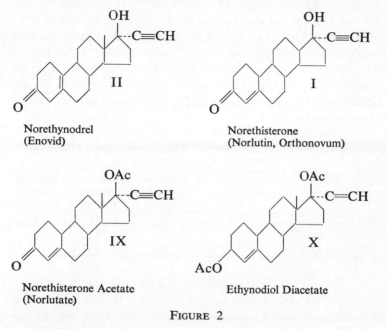

Norethynodrel
(Enovid)

Norethisterone
(Norlutin, Orthonovum)

Norethisterone Acetate
(Norlutate)

Ethynodiol Diacetate

FIGURE 2

In Table VIII are some data of the comparative study that Dr. García mentioned is being carried on by Dr. A. Pendleton Satterthwaite in Humacao (9). The Enovid used has 2.5 milligrams of the norethynodrel, the Orthonovum 2 milligrams of norethisterone, and the ethynodiol tablet has one milligram of its progestin. Each of these is combined with about 1/10th milligram of the estrogen. You will see that in this comparative study 180 to 200 patients have been assigned to each preparation. Dr. Pendleton observed a dropout in the first year of about 35 per cent of the volunteer subjects on the average and a rejection of each method as such by 13 per cent to 16 per cent of the patients. This is a very familiar history now. You start with 100 patients, and by the end of the year, particularly in Puerto Rico, you end up with somewhere between 60 and 70, and it turns out that half of those who have quit have gone to the United States or have become divorced or have gone to another town, and the other half have just said, "I don't want this method, I want another method." Now among the 16 to 13 listed here are patients who transfer to another type of pill, not only to another type of contraceptive. So there is a lot of this "to-ing and fro-ing."

TABLE VIII

Statistics of Comparative Study

	Total No. of patients admitted	No. Discontinuing in 11 cycles	% Discontinuing	% Rejecting method as such
Enovid 2.5 mg	209	76	36	16
Orthonovum 2 mg	209	78	37	13
Ethynodiol 1 mg	182	56	31	13

In Table IX are data from the comparative study on menstrual phenomena in these patients. Again it is rather interesting that these three 19-norsteroids which are chemically closely related seem in this area to be very similar in their action. You see the percentages of women saying that the amount of menstrual flow is light, average or heavy is just about identical in the

TABLE IX

Comparative Study — Menstrual Phenomena — % Reporting

Compound	Amount of Flow			Pain and Distress		
	Light	Average	Heavy	None	Slight	Moderate to severe
Enovid	14	80	6	69	19	12
Orthonovum	18	78	4	68	20	12
Ethynodiol	14	81	5	71	19	10

three groups. The occurrence of pain or distress at menstruation listed as none, slight, or moderate to severe is again for all practical purposes identical in the three groups. These substances all act in a manner which is, in terms of the response of the patient, very similar. Now how much of this is psychogenic and how much is truly physiological is a problem. Dr. García mentioned the fact that we have this so-called first cycle phenomenon of a high incidence of complaints and premature menstruation. This is true with all the ovulation inhibitors of this type that have been studied. In Table X are some data on patients taking ethynodiol diacetate. In the first cycle those who reported reactions, in other words those who complained about something, were 16 per cent of all patients. The percentage with breakthrough bleeding came to 5.6. These incidences declined in the second cycle, and you see that by later cycles you come down to a much lower figure than the first cycle or two or even three. This is a phenomenon which we have repeatedly noted with the use of any of these ovulation inhibitors. This is why we think that there may be a very strong psychogenic element to the so-called reactions and also perhaps even to some extent to the menstrual breakthrough. Initially, with the use of a pill, and these patients have never used pills before, there's some apprehension, some anxiety which finally settles down.

TABLE X

Patients Taking Ethynodiol Diacetate

Cycle No.	No. of Cycles	% with "Reactions"	% with Breakthrough
1	126	15.9	5.6
2	125	9.6	4.0
3	122	9.0	1.6
4	115	4.3	2.6
5–8	402	3.2	2.7
9–16	246	4.9	1.2

No conceptions in 97.4 years of exposure.

TABLE XI

*Responses to Questioning by Ethynodiol Diacetate Users
After 4 to 6 Months of Use*

Concerning	No. of Patients Answering	Percent with		
		Less	No Change	More
Weight	43	37	40	23
Breast size	43	5	88	7
Menstrual flow	44	32	61	7
Dysmenorrhea	42	18	72	10
Libido	44	2	96	2
Coitus	51	39	30	31

April '62

In Table XI we list the answers to various questions that we asked of the patients after a limited use of this new ovulation inhibitor. They give us roughly the same sort of answers had for Enovid originally and which some observers have reported for other ovulation-inhibiting drugs. There is very little significant change during medication in any of the items except in the amount of menstrual flow which on the average appears to be somewhat lighter rather than heavier. Otherwise you see that whatever happens here by and large appears not to be attributable to the drug but simply to the individual patient's reaction. In fact in this study with ethynodiol we took the trouble of asking each patient before she entered the study whether in the course of her previous menstrual history she had any reactions. Did she have such things as nausea, vomiting, dizziness; did she have headaches associated with phases of her menstrual cycle and so on. These were all items that were complained about to a greater or lesser extent. In Table XII are the statistics of what happened when we examined these patients again six months later. Among the patients those who said they had no reaction before taking the medication or during it amounted to 37 per cent of the total. Those who said they never had any reactions before but some during medication amounted to 24 per cent of the total. Those who said they had the reactions before and that these continued to appear during the medication amounted to 16 per cent of the total, and those who had complaints before but none during medication amounted to 23 per cent of the total. Now, I doubt that these figures are significantly different one from the other; perhaps the first is different from the others. At any rate, if you were to make the calculation of what this drug does on the basis of those women who had the reactions before but not during medication, 58 per cent of the patients were cured of their reactions with this drug. On the other hand, if you take the patients who said they never had any complaints before, but had them during the medication, then we induced reactions in 39 per cent of the patients. In other words, as far as I am concerned, the psychogenic element is so strong in the use of any such medication that the talk of serious side effects had better be very carefully examined before one attributes these side effects to the drug.

Finally, at a recent meeting in Singapore of the International Planned Parenthood Federation there was a summary by Dr. Tyler (10) of a number of reports that were made to the meet-

TABLE XII

Patients Reporting "Reactions" to Ethynodiol Diacetate

	Number	% of Total
None before or during medication	45	37
None before but some during medication	29	24
"Reactions" before and during medication	20	16
"Reactions" before but none during medication	28	23
% "cured" of reactions	58.4	
% with "induced" reactions	39.2	

ing on the action of these ovulation inhibitors used as oral contraceptives. In Table XIII are the data for a group of 19-norsteroids. This shorthand is probably straightforward. For example, No. 1 is Enovid used in a dosage of 2.5 milligrams of norethynodrel along with 150 micrograms of the estrogen. Dr. Krisna Menon in Madras studied 75 patients in 692 cycles. He

TABLE XIII

Medical Session Reports (Singapore)
Norethindrone and Norethynodrel Combinations

Product		No. Pts.	Cycles	Results	
(1) Enovid	2.5/150	75	692	Large % side-effects Heavy dropouts	
(2) Enovid	2.5/100	100		1 early failure ?. 1 failure	
Conovid		300	1,626	Mod. side-effects Generally successful	
(3) Conovid	5/75	216	3,267	About 20% dropout	No
"	2.5/100	262	2,718	About 20% dropout	Method
Anovlar	4/50 EE	196	2,093	About 20% dropout	Failure
(4) Ortho-N	10/60	210	8,000	< 1% Rx dropout. No PN	
"	2/100	104	1,100	< 1% Rx dropout. No PN	
(5) Enovid	10/150			17.5% Rx dropout	
"	5/75	838	15,000		
"	2.5/100			13 incorrect use PN	
(6) Ortho-N	10/60	567	16,000		
"	5/75	172	832	About 5% total dropout. 1 ? PN	
"	2/100	412	4,700		
Enovid	5/75	334	10,000	About 10% total dropout. No PN	
"	2.5/150	114	700	About 7% total dropout. No PN	
Gestop	5/50EE	169	3,088	About 5% total dropout. No PN	
"	2.5/50EE	141	571	10% dropout. No PN	

(1) Menon, K. (Madras) (2) Chinnatamby, S. (3) Mears, E., et al. (London) (4) Goldzieher, J. (Texas), Rice-Wray (Mexico), Moses, et al. (Ohio) (5) Satterthwaite and Gamble (Puerto Rico) (6) Tyler, E. T., et al. (Calif.)

had a large percent of side effects and heavy dropouts. Actually, these figures, I think, amounted to something like 45 per cent of the patients dropping out by the end of the year. The use of the same drug with a somewhat lower estrogen content was reported by Dr. Chinnatamby in Ceylon with 100 patients initially, then 300, and now I think with about 800. She had one early failure, which means one pregnancy; which she felt occurred while the medication was being taken, very moderate side effects, few dropouts, and was generally very successful. In India there was a lot of trouble with dropouts, but across the water in Ceylon the dropout rate was extremely low. Thirteen pregnancies due to incorrect use of Enovid were reported by Dr. Pendleton. As we go down the line for these various drugs you can see that, depending apparently on the investigator, in large part the successful use, the dropout rate, and so on appear to be characteristic of the place at which the project is carried out. Thus, Dr. Mears has about 20 per cent dropout for two of these preparations, whereas in other places the dropout may be as little as 5 to 10 per cent with similar preparations. Exactly what this means we are not sure, but it is clear that at least in terms of "conception control" the number of pregnancies is extremely low and the use of several of these 10-norsteroid inhibitors has been on the whole quite successful.

Another group of steroid progestins which have come into prominence in recent years are the so-called 17-acetoxy progesterone derivatives. In Figure 3 are the structural formulae of several under investigation. These are the compounds which are acetylated at the 17-hydroxy. There are various derivatives, methylated at carbon 6, or with fluorine or chlorine at carbon 6. We give the relative potencies of these as ovulation inhibitors in the rabbit in terms of the standard. Among them chlormadinone is the most active. Actually 6 dehydro-methyl derivative is an extremely active compound which has been used under various trade names in contraceptive trials.

ORAL OVULATION INHIBITORS

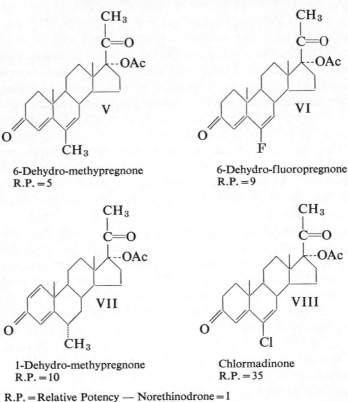

6-Dehydro-methypregnone
R.P. = 5

6-Dehydro-fluoropregnone
R.P. = 9

1-Dehydro-methypregnone
R.P. = 10

Chlormadinone
R.P. = 35

R.P. = Relative Potency — Norethinodrone = 1

FIGURE 3

In Table XIV is the report from the Singapore meeting on the use of some of these compounds in field trials. Chlormadinone, for example, has been used in well over 1000 patients. Its acceptance is quite good. You see there are a few pregnancies in what they call chlormadinone sequential. This sequential treatment essentially involves administering the estrogen, for ex-

TABLE XIV
Medical Session Reports (Singapore)
New Combinations, Progestins or Dosage Schedules

Preparation and Dose	No. Pts.	Cycles	Results
(1) Megestrol (2/.05 EE to 5/0.1 EE) Lyndiol, SC-11800, Norlestrin, and Sequential Chlormadinone	243	996	Generally Good (Statistics to be given)
(2) Chlormadinone (2 mg.)	467	4793	Generally good. No PN
Chlormadinone Sequential	938	6314	Good acceptance. 3 PN
(3) SC-11800 (1/0.1 EE3ME)	163	1500	About 5% total dropout. No PN
Provest (10/0.1 EE, 10/.05 EE, 2.5/.025 EE)	173	1900	BTB excessive. 25% dropout. No PN
Chlormadinone Sequential (2/80)	40	700	About 4% total dropout. 1 ? PN
Ortho-Novum Sequential (2/100)	30	600	About 2% total dropout. No PN

(1) Mears, E., et al. (London)
(2) Goldzieher (Texas), Moses (Ohio), Martinez, et al. (Mexico)
(3) Tyler, E. T., et al. (California)

ample 80 micrograms for 15 days, and then for 5 days giving the progestin at a given dose along with the estrogen. Except for one compound, Provest, listed here, the results are comparable to those obtained with the 19-norsteroids in terms of contraception. The dropout with Provest is very large and this is the compound to which Dr. García referred in saying, "In our hands it appeared to be a very poor ovulation inhibitor and perhaps the worst feature of its use is the excessive presence of breakthrough bleeding, premature menstruation." This is a very hasty summary of where we stand with the ovulation inhibitors.

I'd like to spend a few minutes on some studies of the development of the fertilized egg. In Figure 4 we have in diagrammatic form an indication of the hormonal involvements in the development of the fertilized egg. The ovarian hormones are for the most part involved with the entry of the egg into the uterus, its growth in the uterus and its implantation in the endometrium. As you all well know, it is ovarian estrogen and progestin which prepare the uterus for the reception of the fertilized egg and its implantation. We have been interested in the role of the steroid hormones, particularly progestin, in the production of this pseudopregnant or ovum receptive endometrium. We have chosen to study it initially at least on the basis of certain of the very remarkable changes in the endometrial content of the enzyme carbonic anhydrase.

Carbonic anhydrase is the enzyme which controls the rate at which carbon dioxide combines with water to give carbonic acid. The enzyme has been found in many tissues. Dr. Lutwak-Mann (11) was the first one to point out the very high concentration of this enzyme in the uterus particularly during the luteal

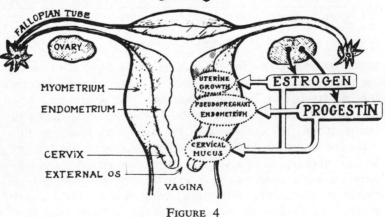

FIGURE 4

phase of a cycle when active progestin is being secreted by the corpus luteum of the ovary. Dr. Miyake and I (12) became interested in this and were encouraged by Dr. Lutwak-Mann's report of an almost quantitative relationship between the amount of progesterone presumably secreted and the content of the enzyme. We used this relationship as a basis for a quantitative method for progesterone assay. Figure 5 shows that this relationship is indeed quite good. The carbonic anhydrase content of the endometrium plotted against the dose of progesterone gives

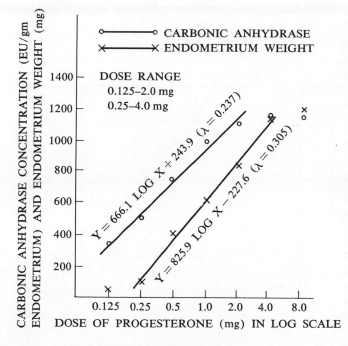

FIGURE 5

you a very excellent log-dose relationship with a lambda, the index of accuracy, which is extremely low and therefore more exact than the response of endometrial weight to the progesterone stimulation. Therefore this is a good method of assay and it has been used quite a lot.

Actually you can use this carbonic anhydrase response of the endometrium for the assay of inhibitors of progesterone. In Figure 6 are the data that we obtained with a constant dose of

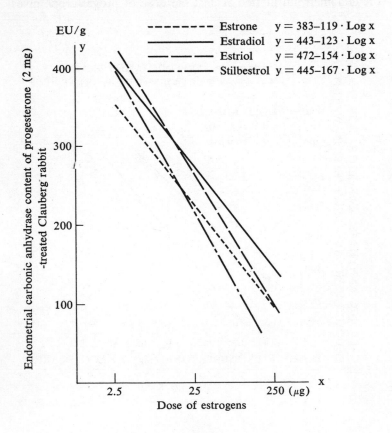

FIGURE 6

progesterone given to estrogen-primed immature rabbits who received various dosages of estrogen against the constant dose of progesterone. Using three of the natural estrogens, estrone and estradiol and estriol, and the synthetic estrogen stilbestrol, we were able to inhibit the effect of the progesterone. For the inhibition we see a linear log-dose relationship. We studied a large number of substances as potential anti-progestins using this method of assay and finally emerged with a fair number which were quite effective (14). Some were especially interesting because as far as we could tell they were anti-progestins but not estrogens. For many years it has been known that estrogens act as anti-progestins in many situations but here we had some compounds which appeared not to be estrogenic at all.

In Figure 7 are the formulae of nine of the compounds that emerged as active progestin inhibitors. Among these the last two, VIII and IX, are quite weak but definite estrogens. Compound VI is a very interesting compound because it is not only an anti-progestin, it is a very weak progestin, i.e., in large dose, and it is also a very weak estrogen, i.e., again only in large dose. Compound IV is also quite interesting; it is a neutral A-norsteroid, i.e., it lacks one of the carbons in ring A. It has strong anti-progestational action, actually one of the most powerful of the lot in our hands, and has a completely saturated steroid nucleus of the androsterone type, if you will, and yet is not an androgen. It is not an estrogen; it is not a progestin; it is an anti-progestin and has also a very weak anti-estrogenic activity.

Dr. Banik and I have tested the nine compounds of Figure 7 as implantation inhibitors (15). This involves administering the material once a day for three days following the establishment of mating in the rat or the mouse. It is evident from Table XV that the first two compounds were inactive in both species in dosages up to 2.5 milligrams per animal. On the basis of their anti-progestational activity these doses should have been more than enough for inhibiting the development of the uterus neces-

ANTI-PROGESTINS TESTED AS IMPLANTATION INHIBITORS

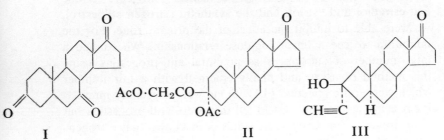

I

II

III

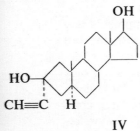

IV

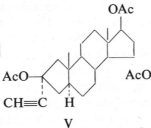

V

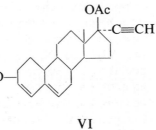

VI

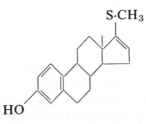

VII

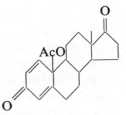

VIII

IX

FIGURE 7

TABLE XV

Steroid Effects on the Implantation of Fertilized Eggs
In Rats and Mice

Compound Number	Animal	Significant Implantation-Inhibiting Dose, mg. per Day
I	Rat	None at 2.5 or less
	Mouse	" " "
II	Rat	" " "
	Mouse	" " "
III	Rat	" " "
	Mouse	2.5 but not 0.5
IV	Rat	0.1 but not 0.02
	Mouse	0.02
V	Rat	None at 2.5 or less
	Mouse	0.5
VI	Rat	0.5 but not 0.1
	Mouse	0.1
VII	Rat	None at 2.5 or less
	Mouse	" " "
VIII	Rat	1.0
	Mouse	0.1
IX	Rat	1.0
	Mouse	0.1

sary for implantation. A number of the other compounds were clearly active; thus IV was especially active, and compound VI not quite so active in these species in preventing the eggs from implanting. We took four of the most potent substances and administered them to either the rat or the mouse on day one of pregnancy in a single dose known to be active when given daily for three post-coital days. Again the same single dose was given on day three only. As can be seen in Table XVI the material administered on day one was quite effective in inhibiting implantation, whereas in several instances where it was administered on day three it was relatively ineffective. This suggests that these substances can be given the day after mating for the most effec-

TABLE XVI

Effects of Single Injections on Ovum Implantation
in Rats and Mice

Compound Number	Animal	Significant Inhibitory Dose (mg) on Day	
		One	Three
IV	Rat	1.5	None
	Mouse	0.1	None
VI	Rat	1.0	None
	Mouse	0.1	0.1
VIII	Rat	1.5	None
	Mouse	0.1	?
IX	Rat	1.0	None
	Mouse	0.1	?

tive inhibition of implantation. Indeed in recent studies with an extremely potent A-norsteroid, implantation inhibiting doses are quite ineffective when administered following implantation. Thus we have the possibility of preventing implantation without the risk of abortion. Presumably such compounds need to be taken only after intercourse to insure implantation failure. A similar action against the preimplantation ova has been shown for a non-steroidal substance by Dr. Warren Nelson (6). This ovicidal material (7) has not proven usable clinically, but the steroids have generally been non-toxic and their future as usable contraceptives seems distinctly promising. So here is another research frontier.

Acknowledgments:

Much of the experimental work described in this paper has been aided by research grants from Mrs. Stanley McCormick, G. D. Searle and Company, the Population Council, and the Andre and Bella Meyer Foundation.

References

1. Parkes, A. S. *This volume,* p. 26 ff.
2. García, C. R. *Ibid.,* p. 43 ff.
3. Soffer, L. J., Futterweit, W. and Salvaneschi, J. J. *Clin. Endocrinol. and Metab. 21,* 1267. 1961.
4. van Rees, G. P. and Walthus, O. L. *Acta Endocr. 39,* 103. 1962.
5. Purshottam, N., Mason, M. M. and Pincus, G. *Fertil. and Steril. 12,* 346. 1961.
6. Purshottam, N. *Am. J. Obst. and Gynecol. 83,* 1405. 1962.
7. Hopkins, T. and Pincus, G. *Endocrinol.* (in press) 1963.
8. Pincus, G., García, C. R., Paniagua, M. and Shepard, J. *Science 138,* 439. 1962.
9. García, C. R., Satterthwaite, A. P. and Pincus, G. *Proc. 6th Internat. Planned Parenthood Conf.* (in press) 1963.
10. Tyler, E. *Ibid.* (in press) 1963.
11. Lutwak-Mann, C. J. *Endocrinol. 13,* 26. 1955.
12. Miyake, T. and Pincus, G. *Endocrinol. 63,* 816. 1958.
13. Miyake, T., and Pincus, G. *Proc. Soc. Exp. Biol. Med. 99,* 478. 1958.
14. Pincus, G. and Merrill, A. *Perspectives in Biology.* p. 56. Cori, Foglia, Leloir and Ochoa (eds.). Elsevier, New York. 1963.
15. Banik, U. K. and Pincus, G. *Proc. Soc. Exp. Biol. Med. 111,* 595. 1962.

THE INHIBITORY ASPECTS
ON GONADS OF THE MALE

WARREN O. NELSON

Formerly Medical Director, The Population Council, Inc., Rockefeller Institute for Medical Research.

ALTHOUGH THE MAJOR SHARE of research in the limitation of fertility has thus far been directed towards the female, I think it is evident that for adequate and complete attention to birth control, all possibilities of voluntary application as such must also include methods applicable to the male. Indeed, at the present time there are various procedures whereby fertility control in the male can be achieved. Prevention of sperm entry into the female tract can be achieved by ligation of the vas deferens, by *coitus interruptus* or by interposing some mechanical barrier, such as the condom. These, of course, are methods that have had acceptance and are used to varying extents among the people of various cultures, but I think you will all admit that these are crude procedures. As our comprehension of the physiologic mechanisms relating to male reproduction has evolved, it has become evident that methods for the control of fertility in the male, based on physiologic principles, are quite feasible.

There are several points in the male reproductive process that are quite vulnerable to interference. For example the physiologic maturation of sperm that is undergone in the epididymis is a possible method. We know virtually nothing of the fundamental mechanisms of this process. Moreover the phenomenon known as capacitation, which occurs after the sperm are deposited in the female reproductive tract and which enhances the capacity of the sperm to penetrate the egg, is another vulnerable point, but again we know relatively little about the basic mechanisms which are involved.

I might cite several other similar possibilities, but I would like to dwell here on the one that presently is the most promising. This is the inhibition of the spermatogenic process itself. As you know spermatogenesis is a complicated series of cell divisions and transformations that occur within the testis. This varies in its duration from one species to another. In the human being for example it is somewhere between 65 and 70 days. In the rat we know very accurately that it is 48 days from the young spermatogonium to the fully matured sperm. We know that sperm formation can be very effectively prevented by inhibiting the secretion of the pituitary gonadotrophic hormones by means of various steroids — the steroids, for example, that Dr. Pincus discussed above. These are equally as effective inhibitors of male germ cell production as they are of ovulation. This method of fertility control in the male is highly effective, but it does not appear to be of practical value as the inhibition of gonadotropins is not selective. The steroids inhibit both FSH and LH and, as a consequence, not only is sperm production inhibited but also the secretion of male sex hormone. This of course lowers both libido and potentia and is not likely to have very enthusiastic acceptance. Studies thus have been carried out on human beings with a number of steroids, for example, Enovid and Norlutin. In a prison population the capacity of these substances to invoke reversible inhibition of spermatogenesis has been demonstrated. However, as I have said, these studies also showed that male sex hormone secretion was inhibited and as a consequence, libido and potentia were reduced.

In a study carried out by Dr. Carl Heller and me, testicular biopsies were secured from a group of volunteers with such well known preparations as Enovid, Norlutin and Nilevar. These biopsies showed normal testicular histology. Subsequently, treatment with one or another of the preparations was given for about eight weeks during which time sperm counts were made regularly and compared with pre-treatment counts. In each case sperm counts dropped to azoospermic levels by the time treatment was terminated. Testicular biopsies were obtained and showed that the spermatogenic process had been halted at the spermatogonial stage. Tubular size was reduced and, usually, the peritubular connective tissue was increased. Leydig cells were reduced to cells resembling connective tissue elements. This profound effect on the Leydig cells was reflected in the reduction of libido and potentia in the subjects.

These profound effects, however, are reversible and about seven or eight weeks after termination of treatment sperm counts showed a significant rise. In some instances they eventually exceeded the pretreatment level, but I doubt that this has any real significance. Potency and libido return and testicular biopsies confirm the observations on both spermatogenic and Leydig cell activity.

I believe that all of us would agree that these various 19-nor steroids are effective antifertility compounds in the male, but would hesitate to suggest that they have much chance for enthusiastic acceptance.

Recently a limited study has been carried out with another steroid mentioned yesterday by Dr. García. This is the progestin-like compound called Provera. A single injection of this material has been reported to reduce sperm counts to very low levels, apparently without a very significant reduction in potency and libido. These studies are as yet, I think, too preliminary for us to be certain as to their usefulness or general application, but they are promising enough to suggest further consideration and attention.

An established method for the physiologic inhibition of spermatogenesis involves the use of certain drugs which act directly on the germinal epithelium without influencing Leydig cell function. The first group of such compounds to be studied were the nitrofurans. These are a series of compounds which have bacteriostatic action and have had clinical application. It has been shown that these nitrofurans can induce a reversible inhibition of spermatogenesis in both laboratory animals and men. Unfortunately, the dose required to do this in men produced unpleasant side effects and their application was scarcely practical.

A second group of compounds related to the nitrofurans in that there is a sulphur rather than an oxygen in the heterocyclic nucleus, the thiophenes, were also shown to be effective. Again rather undesirable side effects were produced and we never seriously considered their use as contraceptives. However, more recently a group of compounds, the bis-(diacetyl) diamines, were evolved by the Sterling-Winthrop Company for their amebacidal activities. When the usual toxicologic studies were carried out it was observed that there was apparently some effect on the testes. Further studies showed that they do indeed effect the testis in exactly the same way as did the nitrofurans. Consequent to that, two substantial series of studies were undertaken on volunteers in two different prison populations. It was demonstrated in each of these investigations that spermatogenesis could be inhibited and that this was completely reversible. Thus, daily ingestion of these compounds caused the sperm count to drop progressively and to reach zero, or very low levels, at about 70 days after the initiation of treatment. This state of infertility could be maintained indefinitely by continued ingestion of the compounds. Sperm counts gradually returned to normal when treatment was suspended and reached approximately normal levels after 80 to 90 days. At levels of 1 gram or more daily the sperm counts dropped to zero. With lower doses the counts were less effectively suppressed, but even with an eighth of a gram per day, the count was very materially reduced and motility was also affected. It is probable that even though a dose of one-quarter of a gram a day does not drop the count to zero the fact that the motility is seriously impaired and practically eliminated would indicate, I think, that at that level these compounds would have been fairly effective contraceptives. Testicular biopsies secured at various times during treatment showed similar pictures after the full effect of the drug had been instituted. As was the case when the nitrofurans were used, the process of spermatogenesis stops at the primary spermatocyte level. You will recall that these are the cells that finally undergo the reduction division whereby the chromosome number is cut by one half. This division is a complicated meiotic process and is impaired or inhibited by the kind of action provided by these drugs. Biopsies taken after withdrawal of treatment showed progressive recovery. In no instance was this repair unduly delayed or incomplete. Leydig cells were in no way impaired by treatment nor was there any evidence of inhibition of male sex hormone secretion. It is interesting to note that this same picture of spermatocytic arrest is rather commonly seen in men who are infertile. Any male whose seminal study shows azoospermia has a fairly good chance of showing spermatocytic arrest in his testicular biopsy. Thus nature has a way of causing the same condition that is induced by certain drugs.

There is no doubt that these compounds are highly effective as male contraceptives. They have however shown rather unfortunate side effects. As I have said, the studies that have been related were done on prisoners — volunteers — and on the basis of these experiments there was every reason to believe that these compounds could have effective contraceptive application. However, when they were given to men who had free access to alcohol a side effect emerged rather rapidly. This involved the exaggeration of the peripheral effects of alcohol and, while the consequences probably could not be regarded as serious, the reaction certainly was an unpleasant one and there appears to be little or no hope that these compounds would have any useful application as contraceptive agents. I might say that research is continuing on these drugs, however, and it is hoped that some method may be found to eliminate the unpleasant side effects. They are known to be due to an interference with acetaldehyde metabolism.

Even more recently laboratory studies have been carried out on another group of compounds. These are dinitropyrroles, which have been synthesized by the Ortho Research Laboratories. Studies with them have been most encouraging since it has been shown that a single oral dose in rats once every four weeks inhibits spermatogenesis completely without reducing male sex hormone secretion. These compounds appear to interfere with spermatogenesis in precisely the same way as was previously demonstrated for the nitrofurans, thiophenes, and bis-(diacetyl) diamines. That is to say, the final stages of spermatocytic maturation are inhibited, so that mature sperm are never formed.

The compound which has been most effective in laboratory animals is diethylcarbamylmethyl -2, 4 -dinitropyrrole (ORF-1616). In a series of studies made with Dr. D. J. Patanelli it was observed that a single dose of 500 mg./kg. in adult male rats resulted in a precisely defined series of cytologic changes. These could be detected as early as 6 hours after treatment and progressed to a stable state by about the eighth day. Although the most apparent effect was evident in the spermatocytes, as was the case with the compounds discussed earlier, additional effects were seen in the spermatids of steps 1–14 which were present at the time of treatment (older spermatids continued development and produced normal spermatozoa). Although morphologic changes could not be detected in the spermatogonia it seems certain that intrinsic damage did occur since the descendants of these cells manifested serious defects and influenced the total effect of the single treatment. Indeed, analysis of the effect of a single dose of ORF-1616 indicated that the compound continued to exert damage on spermatagonia for about one week following the treatment. The total effect, from a histologic point of view, was that a single dose of ORF-1616 caused sufficient damage to spermatids and spermatocytes so as to provoke a period of infertility of approximately four weeks. This calculation was based upon the known duration of the spermatogenic cycle in the rat (48 days), the equally well-known duration of the integral phases of the cycle, and the time required for passage of sperm through the epididymis (10–12 days). It could be predicted, too, that prior to the period of infertility treated males would be fertile for about three weeks — the time involved in maturation of the undamaged spermatids (steps 15–19) and the clearance of these as well as those already in the epididymis at the time of treatment. Indeed, when mating experiments were actually undertaken these predictions were fulfilled. Twenty male rats were given a single treatment and thereafter were provided with opportunities each week to mate with females in estrus. These males produced litters for at least two weeks, and in the majority of cases for three weeks after treatment. However, in no instance was a litter produced for the following four weeks. Fertility did reappear about the fiftieth day in most of the animals and in the remainder during the following week. Semiquantitative studies made on seminal specimens obtained by electro-ejaculation on treated animals provided additional evidence that a single dose of ORF-1616 would induce azoospermia by the third week with reappearance of sperm by the end of the seventh week post-treatment.

Study of the weights and histologic conditions of testes of animals given a single oral treatment showed that recovery had been initiated by the twenty-fifth day. This progressed so that by the seventy-fifth day testicular weight approached normal levels and the histologic pattern, except for some asynchrony of cellular populations, was normal.

Finally, I should like to say that a study was done in which animals were treated, over a period of six months, at intervals of 2, 3 or 4 weeks. In each of these series the subjects were unilaterally castrated at the termination of treatment and the second testis secured 6, 12 or 20 weeks later. It was shown that the treatment interval was of little consequence since both testicular weight and histology were similar at the termination of treament, and recovery progressed comparably in each of the three series.

Thus far the same serious side effects that were seen in human beings with some of the other compounds have not emerged with these particular drugs and it is hoped that we can look forward to trials in man in the relatively near future. If these drugs prove to be as effective in men as they are in laboratory animals and produce no unpleasant side effects it is quite possible that we will have available a method whereby the ingestion of a single pill once every month will control male fertility for any desired period of time. And I expect that we will find other compounds which are also effective in a similar fashion.

I haven't said anything about another kind of compound that can be used in controlling fertility in the male. I am referring here to the so-called alkylating or radiomimetic agents, a group of compounds which have been studied very thoroughly by a number of people, particularly by Harold Jackson in Manchester, England. These compounds are also effective in single doses. They stop the spermatogenic process at the spermatogonium by killing spermatogonia, much as X-rays do. These are most effective, but I rather doubt that they will have little interest except as a research tool. I doubt that we can look forward to their practical use in the human being.

POSSIBLE EASY METHODS

OF THE FUTURE

JOHN ROCK

Clinical Professor of Gynecology, Emeritus, Harvard Medical School; Director, Rock Reproductive Clinic, Inc.

IT MAY *have seemed that we couldn't bring the two sexes together, but I don't know what the problem is if they don't get together and so in spite of the views presented by Dr. Ansley Coale, I think there still is a problem. I take the title of this talk rather seriously. We speak about frontiers. The last two speakers spoke* from *the frontier; I'm* behind *the frontier, and I would place all of you at the frontier. I hope that your active and inventive minds can take all these various little things that I mention* over *the frontier and into the front line.*

As there is need to reduce the birth rates, the growth rates (I assume you agree to that), many methods are necessary. There must be ways which will find acceptability to peoples of all colors, creeds, kinds, religions and for all mores, economic set-ups, domestic set-ups and so forth. I would suggest that the anthropological sociologists, the social anthropologists, or whatever you call them, have taught us in cross-cultural studies that any couple, however devoted, is not only well able to refrain from coitus for a few days but actually does on many more than a few days. And another "if" — Dr. Coale hasn't a patent on the "ifs", — if the motivation is sufficient, I offer the suggestion that such abstention would be much simpler for many, many people than taking a pill, or immunization — injection or what not.

The difficulty with the rhythm method, as we all know, is that women do not indulge in what they call the "curse" with nearly the regularity and predictability which would make our lives much easier. The safety of the rhythm method depends entirely on the accuracy with which the first day of the next period can be foretold. We haven't yet gotten to the point where we can think of precipitating ovulation on any particular day, but it may come. I think it may not come as easily as some people think because as Dr. Hisaw showed very, very clearly many years ago, only susceptible follicles will accept stimulation and the susceptibility takes a certain number of days. If we would precipitate ovulation on Wednesday, the probability is that we would have to apply the stimulus on Monday or Tuesday or perhaps even Sunday — if we work on Sunday. But there would be no effect unless a preparatory phase had already developed within the follicle. But perhaps we could develop that too, which would mean that we would have to start on the Wednesday before, or even sooner than that. So I wouldn't discourage budding efforts to find an ovulatory stimulant.

We have heard a great deal about suppressing ovulation. This is comparatively easy. I think that the great desideratum is a method of foretelling ovulation. We want a method such as will tell us on Monday or Tuesday that ovulation certainly will occur not later than Thursday. Now, human sperm are only good for 48 hours, more or less, certainly not much more than 48. The ovum is susceptible probably for not more than 12 hours after being freed; so we allow 24. This gives us only about 4 days during which coitus might be productive. And if they knew just what four days, I think the motivation in a great many couples would enable them to be continent for that long.

How can we foretell ovulation? I hope that Dr. McArthur will say something about methods of determining the appearance of significant amounts of what we still consider the final stimulus to ovulation — LH, or minimal amounts of LTH. I don't know what form it is that finally causes the strangely obscure opening in the follicular wall. How ridiculous that we don't know what changes a stigma into an aperture, when we know so much about cytochemistry, enzymology in cells, etc. We know a great deal about vascular changes, and all we know really about the rupture is the morphology.

But something causes ovulation, and I have frequently referred to the fact that when I was a medical student, which was back in 1915, I was surprised to find that the urinals — of course there were only men then — in the basement had been, shall I say, altered. In every second stall the urinal had been removed and in its place was a very large glass carboy with a big funnel that came up to just the right height and a sign above it, "Please contribute". Dr. Folin was attempting to improve a method of detecting sugar in urine and he went about it with as much vigor as that; he collected gallons of urine every day and removed all the sugar that was in the urine and then added known amounts to aliquots and then went looking for what he put in. He finally found it and later discovered a very simple method which now enables us just to put a little piece of paper in a basin and tell whether or not there is any sugar in the urine. How very simple it would be if a method were found to detect ovulation by a color test of urine.

We know that in the subprimate mammals the male becomes acutely aware through his nose that the female is about to ovulate. We even see in the cinematographic recordings of monkey behavior that the buck is always smelling around and paying a great deal more attention when he gets just the odor he wants. There are many odoriferous secretions in the female that I think have not been accorded nearly the attention they deserve and it would seem distinctly possible to identify some of the odors that are perhaps peculiar to the preovulatory phase and then evolve methods to detect them.

You are all aware of the work that has been done in the last few years on the cockroach. (I suppose that you know the cockroaches are both feminine and masculine. I thought there was a roach and a cockroach. My better informed and erudite zoological friends, — one of them at least — has told me, "No, no. The genus is cockroach.") Well, you know that the gland in the female cockroach that produces, shall I say, a fragrant substance to which the male cockroach is pecularily sensitive, was identified. The glands were removed and solutions made and from them gases were made; the information was published that these glands produced something which attracted the males, but no one knew what it was. It took a very short time for some biochemists to get to work on the problem. They were not only able to collect the stuff but they were able to identify it and if I'm not mistaken they were able to synthesize it, so that the tiniest little bit, millionths of a part of a solution spread on the cage would collect all the male cockroaches, figuratively, for miles around.

So far as I know there has been no specific work done on humans in this field. Some of you who up to now have thought that you might be going into the study of viruses or of the relief of poliomyelitis, if it needs any more relief, or some of the other viral diseases, or even going into cancer work or something else, might change your minds and go into this problem, which could be much more helpful to the welfare of human beings.

We know that approaching estrus and estrus in mammals is associated with behavioral changes. I may be nearsighted for I can't quite envisage the time when the husband can just tell by cocking his eye, or perhaps listening, what is coming up. You are aware that there are many who know when menstruation is approaching. Not infrequently females make this perfectly obvious. Perhaps they will make the approach of ovulation obvious. I would hope that if they wanted a baby, the manifestation would not be in the same direction as if they didn't want a baby, so that the husband would react adversely to the behavior which was characteristic of the preovulatory phases.

The reversibility of any method of birth rate control, family limitation or family planning is to us, anyway to most of us who are comparatively young yet, a highly desirable quality. There are others, however, who prefer to have it permanent. I think of a man who came into my office some months ago merely to find out where in the United States he could be legally sterilized. I told him I didn't know of any legal block to sterilization but as I looked at him, I had to ask, "How old are you?" "Well, I'm 43." He was a very substantial looking man and very well dressed, obviously quite a person. And I said, "How many children have you?" Well, I was sure he had 7, or 8, or 9 perhaps, but no — he had 3. So, I started off on the regular line, you know; but I didn't get very far when he said, "Doctor, excuse me, I came because I merely wanted to know where I could be legally sterilized. My wife and I have talked over all these little factors and we agreed that this is the way to do it." Then he added, "But it doesn't matter about her anyway, because she has had a hysterectomy." You may laugh at that but I didn't. I was aghast. And I queried, "Why do you want to be sterilized?" Now you can laugh again, because he said: "Well, I don't want to get any other woman pregnant either, do I?" Then he explained it and said that he had four branch offices and he was away from home sometimes 6, 7, 8, 9 weeks at a time. And then I remembered he had said: "My wife and I have talked it all over and we have agreed this is the best way." So that permanence, an irreversible method, was quite desirable to his mind.

Reversibility, however, has been brought up many times. Dr. García mentioned it in regard to suppression of ovulation; Dr.

Pincus as well as Dr. Nelson mentioned it — we all keep this in mind. The one great advantage of an oral contraceptive for women, such as we use, is that if taking the pill is stopped the eggs come back; and they are good eggs. Fertilization is quite possible again.

We have recently been harking back to another method and although I am a gynecologist, I want you to know I'm not hidebound and I do accept suggestions. On the 17th of April in '63 — just a short time ago — I received this note from what I take to be a rural district of Kansas. I quote:

> Dr. John Rock:
> My dear doctor:
> After reading your article in S. E. Post, I can't help but writing you and expressing my opinion. Why stress all preventive methods on us women. Now, you being a doctor know that the male population is the cause of all these babies. After a couple marries and having decided on the number of children they want, have the man altered. There is a very simple remedy that is being used by cattlemen, no cutting, place a clamp on a certain part, it shuts off everything. Now, some husbands to my knowledge have used this method. In after years if there are more children desired, a doctor can remove that clamp and nature functions as usual. I get disgusted when there is so much hallabo (sic) about the care us women should take when it is the men that are to blame for all these surplus babies.
>
> Yours truly,
Mrs. So and So.
>
> P.S. A mother of seven children and a grandmother.

I sympathize with this lady, and I agree with some of her statements.

We have recently been interested in methods of suppressing spermatogenesis that we should have paid attention to right after Carl Moore showed (about 40 years ago) that testes function at a temperature lower than body temperature and if you raise the body temperature, spermatogenesis is stopped. There have been various people who touched and landed in this field and stayed for a short time and took off again. Doctor Watanabe has stirred up a much more active work in this area than did Clarence Gamble who in the 1930's or '40's had obtained some space in the Department of Anatomy at the Harvard Medical School and prevailed upon some of the medical students to come over and subject themselves to hot water, locally applied baths, periodically, and found that sperm counts were notably diminished. He never published his results, nor have I had access to his records; but Dr. Watanabe really went to work on this thing and reported in detail in 1959. I hope he will elaborate on this. I just wanted to mention in passing that with repeated exposure of the scrotum to surrounding heat, in water baths — he had a very ingenious set-up which made it possible to raise the temperature around the scrotum without discomforting the subject — spermatogenesis could be brought down to practically zero, and kept there possibly as long as several months; and when the treatment was stopped, spermatogenesis returned. We have been recently doing this at my clinic. Dr. Naville who has charge of the work has been able to secure, without much effort I may say, the cooperation of many young people around. I'd like to ask him to present his figures.

Dr. Aloys Naville, of Zurich, Switzerland, has since returned to that city.

Dr. Rock mentioned that Moore, in 1928, published his work on sheep; he reported on insulating the sheep scrotum with cotton and found out that the sperm count decreased very rapidly. Meschak did the same thing in 1953 in bulls, and found also that after insulating the scrotum the sperm production was impaired. We tried to do this in humans, a different procedure than the water heating of Dr. Watanabe. To suppress the sperm count we tried to use the body's own temperature and raise the testicular temperature to the body temperature by an insulated scrotal suspensory. First the intrascrotal thermic conditions had to be established by insertion of a thermocouple through a needle into the scrotum and measuring the temperature surrounding the testis. This was done in 35 cases and the average temperature difference between the rectal temperature and the intrascrotal temperature found to be 3.25° centigrade, with a range from 1.8 to 4.7° centigrade. A differential of 1.8° centigrade is very low and was found in only one subject with a varicocele, which is of course another problem. But all other subjects showed at least a 2.5° centigrade difference between the rectal temperature and the intrascrotal temperature. The insulation in the suspensory was found to be best if a cotton-lined plastic pad was used inside the suspensory, the cotton being towards the scrotal skin and the plastic towards the outside. Unfortunately, up to now only two subjects did wear it for a prolonged period 24 hours daily, of course with short interruptions for hygienic and other private purposes. We tested the thermic conditions with this insulator in place in five cases and found that the difference between intrascrotal temperature and rectal temperature was an average of only 1.5° centigrade. In other words the differential is decreased by 1.7° by the scrotal insulation. In two subjects we took the temperature, left the thermocouple in place and then applied this scrotal insulation and found that in 1½ hours the intrascrotal temperature was raised by 2.7° in one case and by 2.8° centigrade in the other case.

One subject wearing the insulation for a prolonged period delivered about 30 control specimens with counts consistently around 150 million spermatozoa per cc, the volume usually being about 6 cc up to 9 cc. Two weeks of scrotal insulation had no effect upon his sperm count, but another two weeks later it decreased to 23 million per cc, still with the same volume. Weekly checks showed a gradual decrease and 3½ weeks later only a very occasional sperm was found in the hanging drop: for all practical purposes an infertile ejaculate. In other words: 7½ weeks of scrotal insulation brought the sperm count down from 150 million to practically nothing. The suspensory was then removed and for five weeks the sperm count was 1 to 2 million per cc; 5½ weeks later it increased to 18 million per cc and another week later it was up to 33 million. Last Thursday it was up to 92.5 million per cc, 8½ weeks after the subject had been taken off the insulation.

The other subject could wear the suspensory only for five weeks because he developed an itching dermatitis, probably from the sweat because he did not change the insulation often enough. The original sperm count was only between 40 and 60 million per cc. After four weeks of scrotal insulation the count decreased to 8 million per cc and after another week to 3.5 million per cc. His insulation was removed and three weeks later the count is still around 1 to 2 million per cc, but we expect him to increase his sperm count in another one or two weeks.

I think this is a very simple method and of course with Dr. Rock as a futuristic thinker, we dream for the future and hope that this easy method of birth control can be developed further. We shall try not to use the suspensory but just give the subject a cotton lined plastic pad and have him wear it under his jockey underwear. The next step would be merely to apply a plastic lining to the jockey underwear.

There has been some casual talk among men who treat infertility and especially male infertility about the dangers of jockey shorts. Except in one case, we have been unable to demonstrate any change in the differential between interscrotal temperature and body temperature in the subjects who were merely wearing the commercial jockey shorts; but if a cotton pad is kept inside the jockey short, the temperature in the scrotum is definitely increased but not beyond a comfortable level.

I want to say one thing about the effect of noise on gonadal function. The best report that I have come across is one of Zondek's who published in late 1960, I think. In short, working with rats, he found that baffling noises particularly affected the female, and increased activity of the sexual organs; but there was a very definite decrease in fertility. The ovaries became larger, the vagina changed, there was more secretion and so forth, but fertility went way down. I mention this largely to bring out a point that has occurred to me about translating laboratory results to humans. It may be that the noise we suffer from could have either a good or bad effect on us — which, I don't know. Perhaps it depends on whether one is a Coale man, or a Rock man. But I think of an analogy such as the effect on glass of a stone thrown by a naughty little boy: if he throws the stone directly at the glass, the glass might break. But if between the glass, or in front of the glass is placed, let us say a mattress, he can throw the stone in exactly the same direction, the glass being in the same place, and the probability is he will not break the glass. I think we must remember in some of these functional areas that there is interposed in humans between external stimuli and their action effect on the organ system an intellectual mattress which might easily change the effect of many of these external stimuli.

Now I shall subside and try to keep my ears open and learn as much as I can from the bright minds in the audience.

SOME FACTS ABOUT

LEGAL ABORTION ‡

Christopher Tietze

Director of Research, National Committee on Maternal Health, Inc.

Induced abortion has been practiced since the dawn of history. In some societies, abortion has been prescribed under certain circumstances; in many, it is tolerated; and in still others, severely condemned. At present, its legal status ranges from strict prohibition and clandestine practice to virtually complete permissiveness through legalization, provided the operation is performed by a physician in a hospital.

In the United States, the laws of most states stipulate a threat to the life of the pregnant woman as the sole legal ground on which pregnancy may be interrupted. This permission is extended, in a few states by statute and elsewhere in practice, to cases where a serious threat to health is to be averted. In many places, certain eugenic indications, such as German measles in the first trimester of pregnancy, are also recognized. The interpretation of the law by physicians and hospital administrators is, as a rule, on the conservative side.

Table 1 shows the numbers of therapeutic abortions performed from 1943 through 1957 in New York City, the only jurisdiction where all fetal deaths must be registered. While the

‡ This presentation draws heavily on several earlier publications by the author (References 10, 11, 12).

reports for later years have not been fully analyzed and published, it is my understanding that no major changes have taken place. The annual numbers of therapeutic abortions in New York City have declined from about 700 in the middle forties to about 300 in recent years; the ratio per 1,000 live births has fallen from 5 to 2. This overall trend reflects a sharp and continuing decline in traditional medical indications, and, at the same time, a substantial increase in the incidence of abortion on psychiatric grounds followed by a moderate drop. The pro-

TABLE I

Legal Abortions by Type of Indication: New York City,
1943–1957

| Year | Number | Ratio per 1,000 live births | | | Per Cent Psychiatric Indications |
		All Indications	Psychiatric Indications	Other Indications	
1943	680	5.1	0.4	4.7	8
1944	689	5.6	0.6	5.0	11
1945	687	5.3	0.6	4.7	11
1946	803	5.3	0.8	4.5	15
1947	733	4.3	0.8	3.5	19
1948	na	na	na	na	na
1949	668	4.3	1.2	3.1	27
1950	na	na	na	na	na
1951	679	4.2	1.4	2.8	34
1952	547	3.3	1.3	2.0	40
1953	472	2.9	1.2	1.7	40
1954	440	2.7	1.4	1.3	51
1955	328	2.0	0.9	1.1	48
1956	328	2.0	1.1	0.9	55
1957	336	2.0	1.1	0.9	53

na = not available

Source: 1943–47: TIETZE, C. "Therapeutic abortion in New York City, 1943–1947," *American Journal of Obstetrics and Gynecology*, 60:146–152, July 1950.

1949–53: *Abortion in the United States* (M. S. Calderone, ed.) New York: Hoeber, 1958. P. 84.

1954–57: Unpublished tabulations of the New York City Health Dept.

portion of psychiatric indications among all therapeutic abortions in New York City has expanded from about one-tenth to about one-half.

No reliable estimate can be made of the number of therapeutic abortions in the United States as a whole. If it is arbitrarily assumed that the ratio per 1,000 live births is the same as reported for New York City in 1957, i.e., 2 per 1,000, the current total would be about 8,500 per year. A rough estimate of this sort can do no more than indicate an order of magnitude.

Legislation and practices with regard to abortion in Canada, the United Kingdom, France, Holland, and many other countries are similar to those prevailing in the United States.

In a few countries, such as Sweden and Denmark, abortion policies are substantially more liberal than in the United States. The first comprehensive legislation on abortion in these countries was enacted in the late 1930's. It provided for a broad extension of the traditional medical indications for the interruption of pregnancy and added new indications that had not been recognized previously. In both countries the abortion laws were subsequently amended and liberalized: in Sweden in 1946, and in Denmark in 1956.

The range of acceptable indications for the interruption of pregnancy is roughly the same in the Swedish and Danish laws. In each instance, the law recognizes a medical indication, an extended medical indication, a eugenic indication, and a humanitarian indication. The medical and extended medical indications require a serious threat to the life or health of the pregnant woman. In Sweden the law specifies that this threat may result from a disease, a bodily defect, or what it describes as "weakness."

The extended medical indication, also known as the "social-medical" indication, allows consideration of the pregnant woman's social environment in the assessment of the threat to her life or health. In Sweden since 1946, the law provides that an abortion may be induced "when it can be assumed, considering the conditions of life of the woman and other circumstances, that her physical or mental strength will be seriously reduced by the birth and care of the child." This indication is generally referred

TABLE II

Legal Abortion in Sweden and Denmark: 1939–1960

	Number		Ratio per 1,000 live births	
Year	Sweden	Denmark	Sweden	Denmark
1939	439	484	5	7
1940	506	522	5	7
1941	496	519	5	7
1942	568	824	5	10
1943	703	977	6	12
1944	1,088	1,286	8	14
1945	1,623	1,577	12	17
1946	2,378	1,930	18	20
1947	3,534	2,240	28	24
1948	4,585	2,543	36	30
1949	5,503	3,425	45	43
1950	5,889	3,909	51	49
1951	6,328	4,743	57	62
1952	5,322	5,031	48	65
1953	4,915	4,795	45	61
1954	5,089	5,140	48	67
1955	4,562	5,381	43	70
1956	3,851	4,522	36	59
1957	3,386	4,023	32	53
1958	2,823	3,895	27	52
1959	3,071	3,587	29	48
1960	na	3,918	na	51

na = not available

Source: SWEDEN: MEDICINALSTYRELSEN. *Allmän Hälso — och sjukvård, 1959.* Stockholm, 1961. P. 70.

Denmark 1939–54: DENMARK: SUNDHEDSSTYRELSEN. *Medicinalberetning for Kongeriget Danmark, 1955.* Copenhagen, 1957. P. 127.

Denmark 1955–59: DENMARK: SUNDHEDSSTYRELSEN. *Medicinalberetning for Kongeriget Danmark, 1959, I.* Copenhagen, 1961. P. 110

Denmark 1960: Data supplied by Sundhedsstyrelsen.

to as anticipated weakness. It is not necessary that disease, bodily defect, or weakness actually exist at the time when the interruption of pregnancy is recommended.

The Danish law prescribes that "consideration is to be given not only to physical or mental illness, but also to actual or threatening states of physical or mental stress, based on an evaluation of all circumstances, including the conditions under which the woman has to live."

Taken together, the medical and extended medical indications account for the great majority of legal abortions in Sweden and Denmark. Further analysis in terms of diagnosis is difficult and possibly misleading, owing to the interaction of somatic, emotional, and social factors. It appears, however, that in recent years between 70 and 85 per cent of legal abortions were performed primarily on psychiatric grounds, including conditions described as "exhaustion."

In regard to the eugenic indication, the Swedish law of 1946 mentions only the hereditary transmission of mental disease, mental deficiency, and other severe illness or defect. The more recently amended Danish law includes damage or disease acquired during intrauterine life. The humanitarian indication, called "jurisdicial indication" in Denmark, applies in the case of pregnancies resulting from certain offenses against the penal code, such as rape and incest, and to pregnancies in children less than 15 years of age.

Examination of the administrative machinery implementing the abortion laws reveals major differences between the two countries. The procedure is highly centralized in Sweden, where about 85 per cent of all legal abortions are authorized by the Royal Medical Board in Stockholm, which has exclusive jurisdiction over cases involving eugenic consideration, or legal incapacity and facultative jurisdiction over all other cases. The remaining 15 per cent are performed on the authority of a certificate signed by two physicians.

The Royal Medical Board makes its decisions on the basis of a written report by the physician who has examined the woman seeking abortion. The format of this report is prescribed, but the detail included varies greatly. In recent years, about half the reports have come from municipal and other publicly supported clinics where psychiatrists and social workers are available for their preparation. Of the requests for legal abortion submitted to it in 1959, the Royal Medical Board approved 65 per cent, compared with 79 per cent in 1954 and 89 per cent five years earlier.

In Denmark, most legal abortions require authorization by a committee of three persons, attached to the local Mothers' Aid Institution, a publicly supported organization, which conducts a thorough medical and social investigation. There are at present about 20 such committees throughout the country. Each consists of a psychiatrist, a gynecologist, and an experienced social worker. A decision for interruption of pregnancy must be unanimous. About 3 out of 5 cases are rejected. Abortions on purely medical indication, where the threat to life and health results from a disease and not from the conditions under which the woman lives, may be performed on the sole authority of the appropriate chief of service.

As a result of the new legislation and its increasing utilization, the number of legal abortions in Sweden increased from about 400 in 1939 to more than 6,300 in 1951. During the same period the ratio of abortions per 1,000 live births rose from 5 to 57. A parallel development occurred in Denmark, pushing the number of legal abortions from about 500 in 1939 to 5,400 in 1955 and the ratio per 1,000 live births from 7 to 70.

In recent years the upward trend of legal abortions appears to have been reversed. In Sweden the number declined from 6,300 to about 3,000 per year, and in Denmark from 5,400 to less than 4,000 per year. The current ratios per 1,000 live births are on the order of 30 in Sweden and 50 in Denmark, while the annual rates of legal abortion are 0.4 and 0.8 respectively, per 1,000 population. In part, this reversal of the trend appears to reflect a more restrictive practice of authorization. It is not clear to what extent other factors may also be involved, such as a change of attitude toward abortions on the part of pregnant women or a more general and more skillful use of contraceptives.

While the laws and practice in matters of abortion are much more liberal in countries such as Sweden or Denmark than they are in the United States, these countries do not have legalized abortion, although many persons in this country believe it. Other countries, notably Japan and a number of countries in Eastern Europe, have adopted far more radical policies and it is to these countries that we shall now turn our attention.

In Japan, the Eugenic Protection Law of 1948 authorized interruption of pregnancy for economic as well as medical reasons. The crucial passage is contained in Article 14 of the law and permits the interruption of pregnancy in a woman "whose health may be affected seriously from the physical or economic viewpoint by the continuation of pregnancy or by confinement." The subsequent interpretation of this paragraph by the medical profession, by the authorities, and by the public has been tantamount to making abortion available without restriction.

As shown in Table III, the reported numbers of legal abortions in Japan rose from 246,000 in 1949 to 1,170,000 in 1955, corresponding to an annual rate of 13.1 abortions per 1,000 population. Since then, numbers and rates have declined slightly. The actual totals are believed to exceed the numbers reported by several hundred thousand, owing — it has been alleged — to the reluctance of physicians to pay income tax on their full earnings. Tax authorities check the number of reported abortions with the doctor's tax return and they ask questions.

TABLE III
Live Births and Legal Abortions in Japan, 1949–1961
(Rate per 1,000 population)

Year	Live Births		Legal Abortions	
	Number	Rate	Number	Rate
1949	2,696,600	33.2	246,100	3.0
1950	2,337,500	28.2	489,100	5.9
1951	2,137,700	25.4	638,400	7.6
1952	2,005,200	23.5	798,200	9.3
1953	1,868,000	21.5	1,068,100	12.3
1954	1,769,600	20.1	1,143,100	13.0
1955	1,730,700	19.4	1,170,100	13.1
1956	1,665,300	18.5	1,159,300	12.9
1957	1,566,700	17.2	1,122,300	12.3
1958	1,649,800	18.0	1,128,200	12.3
1959	1,622,800	17.5	1,098,900	11.9
1960	1,603,000	17.2	1,063,200	11.4
1961	1,586,400	16.9	1,035,000	11.0

Source: 1949–57: MURAMATSU, M. "Effect of induced abortion on the reduction of births in Japan," *Milbank Memorial Fund Quarterly,* 38: 153–166, April 1960.
1958–61: Data supplied by Dr. Muramatsu.

Abortion policy in Eastern Europe has undergone several major changes since November 8, 1920, when interruption of pregnancy at the request of the pregnant woman was legalized in the USSR by a joint decree of the Commissariats of Health and Justice. On June 27, 1936, another decree restricted legal abortion to a list of specified medical and eugenic indications. On November 23, 1955, the policy was once more reversed and the restrictive decree of 1936 repealed by the Presidium of the Supreme Soviet.

Following the example of the USSR, most of the countries of Eastern Europe have adopted similar legislation. The stated aims of this legislation, in the words of the preamble to the Soviet decree, are "the limitation of the harm caused to the health of women by abortions carried out outside of hospitals" and to "give women the possibility of deciding by themselves the question of motherhood."(3)†

Throughout Eastern Europe, official concern with overpopulation or rapid population growth is precluded by Marxist philosophy. Moreover, several of the countries concerned have very low birth rates, and none has a high birth rate by global standards. At least one country (Czechoslovakia) pursues an active policy by means of family allowances for third and later children.

Within the overall pattern of legal abortion, considerable variation between individual countries is apparent. Abortion at the request of the pregnant woman is currently permitted in the USSR, in Bulgaria, and in Hungary. In Poland, the law of 1956 stipulated a "difficult social situation" as an acceptable reason for the interruption of pregnancy and made the physician responsible for the determination of its existence. Since early 1960, however, an oral declaration by the pregnant woman suffices to establish her "difficult social situation."

In Czechoslovakia, the law permits abortion for reasons "worthy of special consideration," among which the Ministry of Health lists these: (a) advanced age of the woman, (b) three or more living children, (c) death or disability of the husband, (d) disruption of the family, (e) predominant economic responsibility of the woman for the support of the family or the child, and (f) a difficult situation arising from the pregnancy of an unmarried woman. In Yugoslavia, interruption of pregnancy may be authorized if the birth of the child "would result in a serious personal, familial, or economic situation for the pregnant woman which cannot be averted in any other way."

Commissions for the authorization of abortion, consisting of physicians and representatives of the social services, have been established in Czechoslovakia and Yugoslavia. Medical boards

† Numbered references will be found on page 236.

also exist in Hungary, but their function has become purely formal since they must now assent if the applicant insists on having her pregnancy interrupted. In Poland, abortion is authorized by a certificate from a single physician.

Abortion is prohibited in pregnancies of more than three months' duration, except for medical reasons. It is also forbidden if the applicant has undergone an induced abortion during the preceding six months.

Interruption of pregnancy must be performed by physicians in appropriately equipped and staffed hospitals, which in Eastern Europe are public institutions. The typical period of hospitalization is two or three days, followed by sick leave if the woman is a wage earner.

As a rule, abortions for medical reasons are performed free of charge, while those done on request or on "social indications" must be paid for by the applicant. These charges cover only part of the costs of the operation and hospitalization. In Czechoslovakia, fees for abortion on social indication were abolished in 1960.

Interruption of pregnancy by unauthorized persons or under unauthorized circumstances (e.g., in a doctor's office) is a punishable offense, but the woman who induces an abortion on herself, or on whom it is performed, does not face prosecution.

The new legislation has resulted in spectacular increases in the incidence of legal abortion throughout Eastern Europe. The most comprehensive statistics are available for Hungary and Czechoslovakia (Table IV). In Hungary strong efforts were made in 1952 and 1953 to enforce existing laws against criminal abortion. These efforts led to an increase in births in 1953 and 1954. About the same time, medical boards for the authorization of therapeutic abortions were established. That these boards progressively liberalized their policies is reflected in the growing numbers of legal abortions from 1953 onward. After the decree of June 3, 1956, had introduced the interruption of pregnancy

Table IV

Live Births, Stillbirths, and Abortions: Hungary, 1949–1961,
and Czechoslovakia, 1953–1961 (Rate per 1,000 population)

Country and Year	Live Births Number	Rate	Stillbirths Number	Rate	Legal Abortions Number	Rate	Other Abortions** Number	Rate
Hungary								
1949	190,400	20.6	4,500	0.5	1,600	0.2	31,600	3.4
1950	195,600	20.9	4,200	0.4	1,700	0.2	34,300	3.7
1951	190,600	20.2	3,700	0.4	1,700	0.2	36,100	3.8
1952	185,800	19.5	3,500	0.4	1,700	0.2	42,000	4.4
1953	206,900	21.5	3,500	0.4	2,800	0.3	39,000	4.2
1954	223,300	23.0	3,700	0.4	16,300	1.7	42,000	4.3
1955	210,400	21.4	3,400	0.4	35,400	3.6	43,100	4.4
1956	192,800	19.5	3,000	0.3	82,500	8.3	41,100	4.2
1957	167,200	17.0	2,500	0.3	123,400	12.5	39,500	4.0
1958	158,400	16.0	2,200	0.2	145,600	14.7	37,400	3.8
1959	151,200	15.2	2,200	0.2	152,400	15.3	35,300	3.5
1960	146,500	14.6	2,000	0.2	162,200	16.2	33,800	3.4
1961	140,400	14.0	*1,900	0.2	170,000	17.0	33,700	3.4
Czechoslovakia								
1953	271,700	21.2	3,200	0.2	1,500	0.1	29,100	2.3
1954	266,700	20.6	3,100	0.2	2,800	0.2	30,600	2.4
1955	265,200	20.3	3,200	0.2	2,100	0.2	33,000	2.5
1956	262,000	19.8	2,900	0.2	3,100	0.2	31,000	2.3
1957	252,700	18.9	3,000	0.2	7,300	0.5	30,200	2.3
1958	235,000	17.4	2,600	0.2	61,400	4.6	27,700	2.1
1959	217,000	16.0	2,400	0.2	79,100	5.8	26,400	1.9
1960	216,900	15.9	2,200	0.2	88,300	6.5	26,300	1.9
1961	218,000	15.8	*2,300	0.2	94,300	6.8	26,000	1.9

* Estimate   ** Hospital admissions

Source: Hungary, 1949–58: HIRSCHLER, I. "Die Abortsituation in der Volksrepublik Ungarn," Internationale Abortsituation, Abortbekämpfung, Antikonzeption (K-H Mehlan, ed.), 114–122. Leipzig: Thieme, 1961.

Hungary, 1959–61: SZABADY, E. "Magyarország népesedési helyzete; a családtervezés gazdasági, társadalmi és egészségügyi vonatkozásai Demográfia, 5:325–332, 1962.

Czechoslovakia, 1953–57: VOJTA, M. "Die Abortsituation in der Tschechoslowakischen sozialistischen Republik," Internationale Abortsituation, Abortbekämpfung, Antikonzeption (K-H Mehlan, ed.), 107–113. Leipzig: Thieme, 1961.

Czechoslovakia, 1958–61: SRB, V. "Pokles potrotuvosti v Československu," Demografic, 4:373–374, 1962.

All data on live and stillbirths from United Nations Demographic Yearbook and Population and Vital Statistics Report.

on request, the number of legal abortions increased rapidly until in 1961 it exceeded the number of live births by more than one-fifth.

In Czechoslovakia, legalization of abortion for non-medical reasons was preceded by almost two years of public discussion. Moderate increases in therapeutic abortions in 1956 and 1957 reflect the changing attitude of the medical profession. Promulgation of a new abortion law in December, 1957, was followed by a steep rise in legal abortions in 1958, continuing at a decelerating pace until 1961. Preliminary figures for the first half of 1962 indicate a slight decline (8).

Legalization of abortion in Eastern Europe has resulted in a substantial body of new information on the risk to life associated with the interruption of pregnancy. Generally speaking, mortality has been exceedingly low. For Hungary, Hirschler's thorough investigation reported 15 deaths following 269,000 abortions during the two-year period 1957–58, corresponding to a mortality rate of 6 per 100,000 (4). The 15 deaths included three attributed to the disease necessitating the interruption of the pregnancy. In these three cases, death occurred in spite of the abortion, not because of it. More recent figures, reported by Szabady for the two-year period 1960–61, point to the even lower mortality rate of 3 per 100,000 legal abortions, based on 9 deaths among 332,000 cases (9).

In Czechoslovakia, a mortality rate of 4 per 100,000 was achieved in 1959–60: there were 6 deaths among 167,000 legal abortions. In 1961, no death was reported (13). In Yugoslavia, according to Mojić, 8 deaths occurred in 1960–61 among 177,000 legal abortions, corresponding to a rate of less than 5 per 100,000 cases. These rates compare most favorably with death rates of more than 60 per 100,000 legal abortions in Sweden and Denmark.

It is almost certain that the lower level of mortality in Eastern Europe reflects primarily the restriction of legal abortion to the first three months of pregnancy, except in cases with medical indication. Abortions at a later stage of pregnancy represent a small fraction of the total number.

In Denmark, on the other hand, legal abortion is ordinarily permitted through the fourth month and in Sweden through the fifth month. In exceptional cases, interruption of pregnancy may be performed at even later periods of gestation. The procedures required for the authorization of a legal abortion are time-consuming. As a result, a substantial portion of legal abortions is performed after the third month. These late abortions contribute heavily to the total number of deaths.

Rates of mortality associated with legal abortion, currently reported from Eastern Europe, are not only much lower than corresponding rates in Northern Europe, but also compare favorably with the risk to life ordinarily associated with procreation. As a rough measure of this risk, I quote the rate of mortality from complications of pregnancy, childbirth, and the puerperium (excluding abortion), computed per 100,000 live births, for white women in the United States in 1959, the latest year for which this information has been published. In that year the rate was 22 per 100,000 — by far the lowest rate among the major countries.

Another standard of comparison of the risk to life associated with legal abortion is the rate of mortality in other elective surgical procedures. The only operations of this type which are performed with sufficient frequency to permit the computation of a stable mortality rate are tonsillectomy and adenoidectomy, usually done at the same time. In the United States, mortality with this procedure is currently on the order of 17 per 100,000 operations.

Owing to the short time since the legalization of abortion, there are no follow-up studies available on late complications and sequelae of legal abortion in Eastern Europe.

While many physicians cling to the belief that interruption of pregnancy, even under the most favorable conditions, often produces sterility, this outcome is, in fact, comparatively rare.

In the United States, I. C. Rubin's study of 1931 is often cited in support of the prevailing opinion (7). Actually, this study is hardly relevant to the problem, as it is concerned with the relative frequency of tubal occlusion among various categories of patients seeking advice and treatment for sterility. Rubin found that the incidence of tubal occlusion was greater among sterile women with a history of induced abortion than it was among sterile women who had experienced a spontaneous abortion or delivery at term or who had never been pregnant.

Neither can one accept as valid the conclusion by Asherman that sterility followed induced abortion in 31 per cent of all cases, as his study is also based on patients with gynecologic complaints (1). Moreover, most, if not all, of the abortions in the histories of these women were criminal abortions.

The majority of recent follow-up investigations of women who had undergone legal abortion, carried out mainly in Scandinavia and ably summarized by Lindahl, have reported an incidence of involuntary sterility between 1 and 6 per cent. Some physicians have been concerned with the psychological after-effects of legal abortion (5). It is true that some women are disturbed about the operation and may even regret it. In Ekblad's carefully studied group of 479 cases from Stockholm, one-fourth reported mild or serious self-reproaches. However, a "closer study of the case-histories of these women . . . shows that even if their subjective sufferings due to the abortion were severe, from the psychiatric point of view, their depression must in general be designated as mild. It is only rarely that the women's working capacity has been impaired or that they have needed to consult a doctor on account of their mental troubles . . ." (2). Moreover, it is necessary to consider not only the possible emotional sequelae of legal abortion, but also the consequences of unwanted parenthood, for mother and child, family and community.

REFERENCES

1. Asherman J. G. "The effects of artificial abortion on fertility," *Proceedings of the First World Congress on Fertility and Sterility,* 2:511–515. New York, 1953.

2. Ekblad M. "Induced abortion on psychiatric grounds; a follow-up study of 479 women," *Acta psychiatrica et neurologica Scandinavica,* Suppl. 99:1–238, 1955.

3. Field G. "The re-legalization of abortion in Soviet Russia," *New England Journal of Medicine,* 255:421–427, 30 Aug. 1956.

4. Hirschler I. "Die Abortsituation in der Volksrepublik Ungorn," *Internationale Abortsituation, Abortbekämpfung, Antikonzeption* (K-H Mehlan, ed.), 114–122. Leipzig: Thieme, 1961.

5. Lindahl J. *Somatic Complications Following Legal Abortion.* Stockholm: Svenska Bokförlaget, 1959, pp. 182.

6. Mojic A. "Abortion is a method of family planning." Paper presented at the IPPF Regional Conference, Warsaw, 1962.

7. Rubin I. C. "Sterility secondary to induced abortion with special reference to tubal factor," *New York Journal of Medicine,* 31: 213–217, 15 Feb. 1931.

8. Srb V. "Pokles potratovosti v Československu," *Demográfie,* 4:373–374, 1962.

9. Szabady E. "Magyarország népesedési helyzete; a családtervezés gazdasági, társadalmi és egészségügyi vonatkozásai," *Demográfia,* 5:325–332, 1962.

10. Tietze C. "Legal abortion in Scandinavia," *Quarterly Review of Surgery, Obstetrics and Gynecology,* 16:227–230, Oct.–Dec. 1959.

11. Tietze C. "The current status of fertility control," *Law and Contemporary Problems,* 25:426–444, Summer 1960.

12. Tietze C, Lehfeldt H. "Legal abortion in Eastern Europe," *Journal of the American Medical Association,* 175:1149–1154, 1 Apr. 1961.

13. Vojta M. Private communication.

DISCUSSION

DR. GREEP *opened the discussion by commenting that "as is usual in a discussion of this type we have treated two people in the audience as computers. We have been feeding this material into these two computers and have posed certain problems to them and we are interested in learning what will come back. For the first discussor of these presentations we will call on Dr. Parkes."*

DR. PARKES: It is almost impossible to keep up the string of metaphor and simile with which we have been bombarded. A few minutes ago Dr. Tietz referred to himself as the caudal end of a program, and I was wondering in what anatomical terms he would refer to me. Perhaps he would agree that I am out on a limb! Coming back to the main metaphor of this discussion, I must say that I feel that I'm not merely up to the frontier, I'm over it.

This has been a most exciting Symposium. I have learned a great deal. Turning first of all to Dr. Nelson's contribution, I was extremely interested to hear about the recent developments in the study of the anti-spermatogenic compounds and to know that something which may be practically applicable is in sight. To judge from what is going on in England at the present time, it will be necessary to provide good evidence that there is no likelihood of genetic effects from this interruption of spermatogenesis. I very much hope that Dr. Nelson will be able to provide such evidence and kill at the very beginning what will undoubtedly be a criticism in England.

Turning now, if I may, to Dr. Rock. I admired his contribution, or should I say performance, very much indeed and I was particularly interested in his suggestion that we should turn our attention from suppressing ovulation to getting rid of it prematurely. I think there may be a great deal in this idea and I hope that it will be followed up.

Several things mentioned by Dr. Rock intrigued me greatly. For instance, the idea of an olfactory detection of ovulation in women was new to me. It is perfectly true of course that in almost all the lower mammals the male detects the estrus condition of the female by olfactory signals and this means that usually he is detecting the time of ovulation. Whether that could ever be applied in the higher mammals, in which sexual receptivity is not restricted to the time of ovulation, I don't know, but it is an interesting thought. It interested me particularly, of course, because my own current research is primarily concerned with olfactory stimuli in mammalian reproduction.

This brings me to Dr. Pincus' observations on the control of implantation. The first point here is whether preventing the implantation of an already fertilized egg can strictly be called contraception and that of course depends on what you mean by conception. I have said this before and I shall undoubtedly say it again, that in my view as a biologist, conception means implantation of the fertilized egg and that contraceptive methods therefore can properly be applied up to that stage. I base my view on the very simple fact that no one says that the hen conceives when her egg is fertilized or that she aborts when she lays it.

Implantation, of course, as Dr. Pincus pointed out, depends on the endometrium being in a receptive condition, a condition brought about by proper balance of estrogenic hormone and progesterone. It has been known for very many years that the overwhelming of the postovulatory progesterone by excessive estrogen would prevent the proper condition developing and would prevent the inception of pregnancy. In fact I have been very much surprised that since the crystalline estrogen became available thirty years ago there has been, so far as I know, no determined effort to see whether the administration of estrogen during the third week of the human cycle would prevent any implantation that might otherwise take place. It would be a difficult experiment to control but if it hasn't been done I certainly think it ought to be done now. Even though estrogens have a bad name, except for essential therapeutic purposes, I still think that this would be a worthwhile experiment. However, there is of course another way of dealing with the postovulatory progesterone. Estrogens prevent the local action of progesterone on the endometrium but possibly a better way of upsetting the balance would be to cut off the supply of progesterone at the source by preventing the proper development of the corpus luteum.

So far as I know, a direct attack on the developing corpus luteum has not been reported, but indirect attack by cutting off the supply of either LH or LTH is undoubtedly effective and can be done, as Dr. Nelson pointed out, by various compounds which inhibit the pituitary gland, probably through the hypothalamic mechanism. All those methods involve something happening primarily within the animal itself.

What about cutting off the supply of LTH or whatever is necessary for luteal development by external factors? This, of course, brings me back to the Bruce effect of pregnancy block in mice, about which I have already commented. In this context, therefore, I want to elaborate a little on the Bruce effect. Bruce's essential observation was that 80 or 90 per cent of newly mated female mice fail to become pregnant if they are exposed to the proximity of males of a different strain from that of the males with which they had mated. The optimal duration of exposure to the proximity of the alien males is three days, and various experiments have indicated that the operative factor is the smell of the alien male. This is an exteroceptive factor working through slowly acting neurohumoral channels. It is not a direct neural effect.

The olfactory block operates up to the time of implantation and is essentially not a block to pregnancy, but a block to implantation. It is prevented by the administration of prolactin (luteotrophin) while the female is exposed to the alien males and it almost certainly arises therefore from a block to luteotrophin secretion by the female's pituitary, and thence from the failure of the corpus luteum of ovulation to develop into the corpus luteum of pregnancy. Probably, a whole chain of reactions is involved, starting with the reception of the smell of the alien males by the chemoreceptors of the female and working through the hypothalamus, the pituitary, the corpus luteum to cause failure of progestational development of the endometrium and failure of implantation.

This raises very interesting questions as to the nature of the odorous substances in mice and as to whether there are similar effects in other species. We don't, in fact, have any idea of what the substances are, although they are almost certainly excreted with the urine of the males. There is obviously an enormous scope for what might be called chemotherapeutic screening of all kinds of likely substances. The second interesting thing to emerge from this, I think, is that although we don't know what these odorous substances are, they obviously belong to a group of substances which is now coming into prominence and which forms a very interesting contrast to the hormone group.

Hormones are secreted into the circulating blood and serve to integrate the individual. These externally secreted substances are exactly the opposite; they are secreted to the exterior and are picked up by another individual and serve to integrate, not the individual, but a population of individuals. Such substances include, of course, not only the mouse smells which act as extraceptive factors, but also the sex attractants which were referred to by Dr. Rock as well as various other compounds which are externally secreted and affect other individuals in various classes of animals. The name, pheromone, has been suggested by Butenant for substances of this type. I like to think that, in contrast to endocrinology which had tremendous innings over the last forty years, we are now witnessing the birth of a nicely contrasting subject, exocrinology.

Dr. Greep then introduced Dr. García.

I have always felt and I was very glad to hear Dr. Rock reiterate that no one method for the regulation of fertility should be applied or be championed as the method of choice. There should be many methods of fertility control available and these should be selected according to the likes and dislikes of the particular country, community and, even more important, to the particular couple that is involved.

Much work by many, many more workers in the area of reproductive physiology is of utmost essentiality if we are going to arrive at methods of fertility regulation for family limitation that are going to be applicable and acceptable. This means applying or extending these investigations to the human. Many of these have been mentioned as possibilities at this meeting and their direct application may prove fruitless in the human. Now, investigations with human subjects is always more trying and the limitations more cumbersome. Collaboration between the clinician and the basic scientist is essential. Sacrifices must be made by both. The clinician must give greatly of himself to gather a human colony and develop it so that while they receive fair and ethical treatment, sufficient subjects may be made available for investigations. It is so much easier merely to practice medicine. The basic scientist is effervescent with thoughts, ideas and suggestions which he has studied in the laboratory and which might be applied to the human. Moreover, he is always mindful of the need for careful, controlled and statistically sound research. In his facilities he can test and evaluate these in the test tube or with the aid of animals, etc. Yet much too often the scientist prefers to purchase his laboratory animals which are not only easier to come by but also lend themselves to more complete evaluation than the human. Earlier we heard Professor Hisaw point out the paucity of primate investigators. The day of reckoning will come. Information from animal experiments cannot be transferred blithely to the human.

The rapport between the clinician who must supply as well as minister to the human subject and the basic scientist who has the know-how and the facilities to arrange and carry out these heralding experiments must be of the highest. Neither should be relegated to the position of sample procurer nor sample analyzer. Both should confer to review and discuss their findings with frequent regularity. In essence, collaboration is essential and must be carried out selflessly. The population problems and social pressures demand it.

Many are the pitfalls that an investigator faces if his human material is not properly selected and not handled by a seasoned clinician with a sound understanding of the problems, and likewise if the laboratory work is not carefully supervised by an expert. Unsupervised selection of patients or patient material by an intern, or laboratory work carried out by a relatively unsupervised technician often has led to many false conclusions.

It is indeed most rare to find an individual who truly can accomplish the work of both the clinician and laboratory scientist. The ability to supply the proper subjects in sufficient numbers and possession of the faculty to carry out laboratory investigations represents major tasks in each area. Attempting to improve one usually lowers the efficiency and caliber of the other. In the words of Woodrow Wilson, "We are in this world not for ourselves but for others." More of us should give this more thought and the progress in human investigation would be accelerated.

The time will come when there will be an array of fertility regulating methods available to meet the exact requirements of the specific couple. This will not be unlike the selection of an antibiotic or chemotherapeutic agent for use in combating the specific bacterium or agent which is afflicting the individual.

The area of the central nervous system has been mentioned repeatedly. Lest the progestins be overlooked, may I say that the work of Sawyer and also that of Flerko indicates a central effect. Another simple piece of evidence is indicated by the thermal rise that they exhibit. The effects of these substances are multifaceted. There are many areas and many end organs that they affect and therefore a great deal more work has to be done in understanding even these methods that we are now using. I thought someone would have mentioned something further after my previous comments concerning the coil. I do not have any personal experience with this method, and perhaps we can impose upon Dr. Tietze to say a few words in his regard.

Now with regard to the detection of ovulation to which Dr. Rock referred, this area of investigation deserves considerable attention since this approach would be acceptable to so many. I am sure, of course, that he was referring to the efforts directed to the detection of impending ovulation. Let us explore the social restrictions implied or required. Sexual continence need be prescribed for the interval of time of sperm survival in the female reproductive tract and correlated with the span of ovum receptivity. This period of self-imposed abstinence may vary considerably, however. Sperm survival varies greatly from couple to couple. The capriciousness of ovulation is legion, and the time interval during which a human ovum is fertilizable is unknown. However, there is some suggestion that the human ovum is probably fertilizable during a span of some twelve hours. Thus if it were possible to ascertain impending ovulation, this method then could be tailored further according to the sperm survival time for the specific couple. Then, of course, reduction of the male libido for this interval would greatly enhance the effectiveness of this method. Lest we forget, the female would also benefit from similar therapy.

I am intrigued by Dr. Rock's and Dr. Naville's comments and observations concerning the effects of heat on spermatogenesis. In this age of gadgets, will the future show us individuals wearing thermal suspensories with batteries and resistors?

DR. GREEP: Dr. Tietze wishes to make a comment about a particular type of device.

DR. TIETZE: I would like to say a few words concerning the intrauterine contraceptives about which we have heard so much in the past few days. Of course I didn't bring this kind of contraband into Massachusetts. When the question came up yesterday a resident of the State, who shall remain nameless, volunteered to procure these objects from an unknown source. The intrauterine devices have a long history. They achieved a short-lived fame with the publication by Gräfenberg in Berlin of his silver ring. His device was a silver spiral shaped in the form of a ring, usually 17.5 millimeters in diameter, which was placed into the uterus and prevented conception in most cases. We don't know how these devices work. The prevailing opinion seems to be that they interfere with the implantation of the ovum, but this is by no means established and work is under way to find out. Gräfenberg published in 1929 and there was a wave of excitement in the contraceptive world about a device that could be put in place and forgotten and would not require any further attention on the part of the couple. Soon, however, the Gräfenberg ring came into disrepute; undeservedly, I think. Since 1959 the medical profession has shown renewed interest in intrauterine devices and a good deal of experimentation is under way. New materials and new shapes are used. The old silver ring has been replaced by a stainless steel ring which Herbert Hall in New York City has used for many years with excellent results.

Some of the newer types of intrauterine contraceptive devices, known as the Lippes loop and the Margulies spiral, are made of polyethylene. The Margulies spiral has an appendage or "tail" with seven small beads which passes through the cervix and protrudes from the external os. The purpose of this appendage is to permit self-examination so that expulsion of the device will be more certainly detected by the wearer. To introduce this device into the uterus, one uses an instrument of flexible plastic material that looks like a straw for drinking lemonade. The instrument is so thin that it can be inserted without dilating the cervix in a nulliparous uterus, and the patient doesn't feel it. The spiral can stay in the inserter for as long as three minutes and still promptly resume its original shape. A metal plunger is used to push the device from the inserter into the uterus. Then the inserter is pulled out and all beads except one that stick out from the external os are cut off. The wearer is taught to check the last bead every week or so. We think the spiral can stay in the uterus for an indefinite period. The Lippes loop is very similar and requires a very similar inserter. It is equipped with a thin plastic thread which is left hanging into the vagina. Most women can be taught to palpate this thread.

The effectiveness of intrauterine contraceptives is very high. Generally speaking, the pregnancy rate runs between one and three per hundred years of exposure. In other words, these devices approach the use-effectiveness of the oral contraceptives. The really important question concerns their ultimate safety. We, that is those of us who have been associated with this work, believe that the side effects allegedly associated with intrauterine contraception, and especially the danger of infection, have been greatly overestimated. A considerable program of research is going on in the United States as well as elsewhere to learn more about this point. Some of this work is exceedingly interesting. Professor Willson and his associates at Temple University in Philadelphia have studied the bacterial flora of the uterus and have found that before insertion of intrauterine devices, about half of the uteri showed no bacterial growth while from the other half a variety of organisms could be cultivated. The same was true after insertion of the device. The numbers of uteri that changed from negative to positive and from positive to negative were on the same order of magnitude. Some women have, of course, acquired gonorrhea while wearing an intrauterine contraceptive. At first, when this work started, it was accepted procedure to remove the device and, incidentally, the removal is very easy because

of the "tail." Of late most of the men working with these devices have given up removing them in cases of infection but give large doses of antibiotics and leave the spiral or loop in place. By way of a modest commercial, I should like to state in closing that the Population Council sponsored a conference on this subject about a year ago, the proceedings of which have now been published under the title, "Intra-uterine Contraceptive Devices," as No. 54 of the International Congress Series of the Excerpta Medica Foundation.

VI

SOCIO-CULTURAL ASPECTS
OF POPULATION GROWTH

CORA A. DU BOIS, Ph.D.

Chairman: Louis Levin, Ph.D.

DR. LEVIN *commented in introducing Dr. Du Bois:*

"Probably I really do not need to introduce this final session, because, in a real sense, Dr. Hisaw has already done this, perhaps better and more fluently than I might. Possibly what I ought to do is to ask him to come up and repeat some of the things he said, but I won't impose double jeopardy on him. Instead, I want to take slight exception to one idea he tossed out. He spoke in terms of the overpopulation problem and said that if man doesn't take care of this problem with his intellect, ruthless nature will do so of her own accord. Though I have been a long-time respecter and admirer of Dr. Hisaw and have a great deal of affection for him, I want to take one slight exception to his diagnosis.

"I doubt that ruthless nature will have an opportunity to take care of the problem. It seems to me that if we have the problem we are talking about — if we are truly going to have overpopulation to the extent estimated — then man with his intellect will take care of it himself by using that intellect. Perhaps I would be more correct if I said by misusing it. It seems to me that man has demonstrated over the ages that he is an aggressive and

competitive sort of animal and when things get really rough he does not hesitate to take things in his own hands. Man now has means of overkill whereby significant reductions in population can be swiftly effected. Some men may take the notion that they can solve the problem to their advantage with some of the equipment, hydrogen bombs and such, that man has designed for himself. Now, possibly this is in a sense the nature of man and therefore perhaps Dr. Hisaw's point is correct. Possibly this is nature's way of taking care of the problem. It has given man implements whereby he can exterminate a large portion of the population if it becomes necessary. Obviously none of us want this. So, in his major point, Dr. Hisaw was, of course, correct. Man must use his intellect to solve this problem intelligently and in a civilized way and to do so he has to consider the nature of man and of men.

"During the meeting we've talked a great deal about the biological and medical aspects of man and there have been some papers and discussion about certain of the sociological aspects. These sociological aspects — and I believe Dr. Hisaw referred to them as the whims of man, the customs, the mores, the religions, the taboos, the emotions and so on — of course, all these enter into this problem of overpopulation in a significant manner. We need only remember that the population explosion, if there is such or if there will be one, is in great measure the result of some of these customs and mores and social and societal factors.

"In his book, The Time Has Come *(Knopf, 1963), Dr. Rock has taken up at least one of these sociological problems and has probed it in considerable depth. I want to commend this work most highly to those who haven't yet had an opportunity to read it. It probes deeply into some of these social and ethical kinds of problems related to the impending population explosion.*

"These are the kinds of important matters which will provide the subject of the discussion at this Session. We have a speaker

who is eminently qualified to talk to us about them — Dr. Cora Du Bois, who is Professor of Anthropology at Harvard University. She is a graduate of Barnard, Columbia and the University of California at Berkeley. She has had a most illustrious career of research and teaching in anthropology and of service to the federal government, and she has been honored for her work not only by our government but also foreign governments."

SOCIO-CULTURAL ASPECTS
OF POPULATION GROWTH

Cora A. Du Bois

Zemurray-Stone-Radcliffe Professor of Anthropology, Harvard University.

I HAVE BEEN steadily misrepresented. It began last January when Dr. Greep persuaded me against my better judgment to undertake this task. I assured Dr. Greep at the time that I know nothing about population growth. That was last January and I'm afraid the situation hasn't changed. Also, I am discovering that there are both rewards and hazards in being the last speaker on the program. Out of my ignorance I prepared an argument which I shall develop in a moment but during these sessions I have been greatly gratified to find some of the arguments that I developed *in vacuo* being sustained by my distinguished predecessors on this program. That is a consolation to me but on the other hand much that I may say at this late point will seem repetitious.

I am engaged in what may seem a presumptuous line of reasoning that leads to a possible strategy of population control. You understand, of course, that this is purely an armchair enterprise to which I shall be happy to have your more practical and informed reactions.

Let us begin, not with one cliché but two: "the population explosion" and "the revolution of rising expectations."

It is quite clear that both of these clichés nevertheless represent very real series of phenomena that are abroad in the world today. It is equally clear that these two clichés express processes that are working at cross purposes.

The increases in the populations of some countries that have already occurred are threatening the aspirations of some of those developing nations to provide a higher standard of living for their impoverished masses. In India, for example, some of her most distinguished economists are arguing that the standard of living for her people has already declined despite a rising gross national product. Some predict a continuing downward trend in that direction. And yet India's annual rate of growth as you know is not by any means one of the highest in the world. It is an absolute increment of 9 million people annually that makes the problem so staggering. That is testing to the full the skill of India's astute planners and humane and democratic leadership.

Faced then with these two apparently self-cancelling trends — the rapid growth of population on the one hand and the rise of expectations on the other — some very sanguine people see a resolution in what they consider to be an equally rapid growth of technological and scientific developments. Certainly science and technology can, and indeed they have already, ameliorate to some degree and in some areas the double bind in which we find ourselves. Yet, clearly, the discussion to which we have been listening these last two days indicates that no amount of technical and scientific ingenuity is likely to meet and cope with the horrifying geometric progression of population increases which, extrapolated on a world-wide basis, tend to swamp us. Dr. Parkes has properly stressed, I think, this point of view, and it must not for a moment be overlooked.

But the ultimate dynamics of population growth and control, despite certain macro-social aspects, rest, I believe, ultimately in micro-social and micro-cultural relationships between human beings.

Before going any further let me make sure that we all understand the terms "social" and "cultural" that were used in the title given me and which I shall be using in the course of my remarks this afternoon. I would never dare stop and make such definitions if Dr. Tietze had not warned me and all of us that sometimes we talk at cross purpose. Most briefly said, a society is an interacting group of people. Society can be analyzed in terms of institutions, roles and interpersonal relations. A culture on the other hand is a consensus of meaning in a population; and so aspects of culture are what people value or disvalue, what goals they generally agree upon, what they consider normative and what they see as good and bad.

Now, let us go back to our main thread of argument. If one assumes, as I do, that socio-cultural factors, and not purely biological ones, are of paramount importance in stemming population growth, both optimistic and pessimistic implications may be drawn.

On the optimistic side is the fact that men's beliefs and attitudes, their personal relationships, their values — in other words, their society and their culture — change more frequently and more rapidly than their biologic constitution. Furthermore, those beliefs and attitudes, those personal relationships, those life-views have repeatedly not only altered in the world's history, but have in altering molded man's procreative behavior and his views of the family. If I am right that socio-cultural factors are of paramount importance in affecting population growth, then, by the same token, one may at least hope for alteration.

On the pessimistic side, however, we know much less about the mainsprings of human behavior and the sources of change in human society and culture than we know about human biology. The so-called science of human behavior is largely still an expression of faith, or perhaps at least a sketch on an academic drawing board. We do not know with any precision how changes in society and culture occur. Nor do we know when deliberately induced changes are attempted whether they will be accepted; or if accepted, how to predict with any assurance what their reverberations will be in any particular socio-cultural population.

I had occasion recently to review the very extensive case material in anthropology on socio-cultural change. The theoretical and conceptual disarray in that literature, I can assure you, is monumental. It represents a mass of contradictory and disparate case studies which were neither additive nor comparable. For example, under a proposition such as the one that an innovation, to be acceptable, must be compatible or congruent with the existing socio-cultural system, different authors have argued from field studies and with equal cogency antithetical conclusions. On the one hand an author will assert that an innovation to succeed must be congruent with existing patterns of behavior and belief. Whereas, on the other hand, another writer has argued with equal conviction that congruence is irrelevant to the acceptance or rejection of innovation. It has even been suggested by one writer that innovation is more readily accepted if it is wholly extraneous to the pre-existing society.

I have no intention of burdening you with the problems facing anthropologists in arriving at a theory — or what I feel is more likely multiple theories — of socio-cultural change. I have digressed simply to illustrate how little we really know in a general and predictable fashion about processes of alterations in human behavior. And yet, unfortunately, this is the question most often put to us by practitioners. It would be so nice to have a little formula to hand over.

Poor as our theoretical equipment may be, I believe nevertheless that we do have a sufficient array of knowledge, certain varieties of categories and concepts that can help us. Or at least that will be better than blind activism.

Let us begin then by carrying the next step of my argument along by bearing in mind three generalizations about cities, the validity of which I believe is assured.

First: History clearly indicates that great cultural fluorescenses and great cultural revolutions usually begin in urban societies. With remarkable consistency it is in the cities that changes begin. They then spread to the hinterlands.

Second: There is wide agreement that fertility rates are generally lower in cities than in rural areas. As we shall see later this generalization needs to be qualified, but let it go for the moment. It does seem certain that growing cities do not enlarge through the breeding of their own population but through immigration from rural areas.

Third: It appears highly probable that more and larger cities will be an irreversible, if deplorable, trend in all countries during the rest of this century.

With these three statements in mind: that cities are breeders of socio-cultural change, that they generally have lower fertility rates than their hinterlands, and that they are certain to grow in size and numbers, I should now like to propose five major categories of societies: tribal, peasant, proletarian, urbanized white collar, and aristocracy. Let me briefly tell you what I mean by these five categories. I can assure you that these are not standardized, operating categories among my colleagues and I doubt that most of my colleagues would accept them.

By tribal societies I mean primarily small, relatively homogeneous, non-literate peoples whose social structure and political power is largely based on real or fictive kinship ties.

By peasant societies I mean agricultural populations who have been described by Alfred Kroeber as "part-cultures" — meaning that they depend primarily for their cultural, and to a lesser extent for their social behavior and beliefs on influences emanating from cities. In Robert Redfield's terms peasants are bearers of the Little, or the Folk Tradition in contrast to urban centers that are creators and bearers of Great Traditions.

By proletarian society I mean the class of wage earners in urban centers who have no reserves or capital other than their own usually unskilled labor. Please understand that I am using the term in just this sense — as it is defined in political science and in Webster — and devoid of its Marxian connotations.

The term "white collar" society is even less satisfactory in its connotations than the term proletarian since it conjures up the image of modern western "office" workers. But I am at a loss to find a better term to describe this particular category of urban society which consists of intellectual, administrative, commercial, and entrepreneurial occupations, with varying degrees of schooling, that sets the model for urban life and that controls, if not ultimately at least in varying degrees, the power, authority and wealth centered in cities.

The term aristocracy is also used in a broader sense here than is usual. I do not mean exclusively people with hereditary positions of privilege but I include also persons who have achieved privileged positions. Whether such persons actually reside in the urban centers or on rural estates, they are bearers and representatives of the Great Tradition.

I have struggled to make these distinctions because I am convinced that the day is past when we can profitably analyze population growth by ignoring social and cultural modes of life. I am convinced that confusion is only confounded by lumping together tribal, peasant, proletariat, white collar and aristocratic populations. Frank Lorimer's *Culture and Human Fertility,* which you remember was prepared for UNESCO in 1954, clearly pointed up the need to operate with more sharply conceived and yet cross-cultural categories. I understress the fact that we need cross-cultural categories. Neither isolated ethnic studies, nor world population studies, useful as they may be for *some* purposes, have much use for tackling the problems of population control.

Pursuing our analysis, and presuming that we wish to work out a strategy both of action and of research to reduce the rate of population growth, I feel that we may disregard both tribal and aristocratic societies. This does not mean that there do not occur occasionally serious problems among tribal peoples, if not among aristocracies, of overcrowding, nor that such pressures do not need the wisest form of administrative handling. What I mean is that neither tribal peoples nor aristocracies seem at the moment to be great reservoirs of population growth. Nor are either of these two groups strategic foci of change in the modernizing world (granted of course that exceptional leaders and innovators may emerge from both of them).

If we are to pursue a strategy of action and research we must ask two questions: Where are the great reservoirs of population growth? Where are the greatest potentials for change?

In developing nations, at least, clearly the two great reservoirs of population growth are the peasantries and the proletariats. If the reservoirs of population growth are in these two categories, is the strategy of action and research to make a frontal attack on these groups and bring all efforts to bear on convincing them of the desirability of family planning? Common sense would certainly seem to indicate such a procedure.

Yet, let us stop to think a moment, particularly since I have learned to distrust common sense as usually reflecting buried and unquestioned assumptions that need to be taken out and aired.

Peasantries are rarely, if ever, initiators of change. As I said earlier, they are part cultures, bearers of little traditions. Their views and opinions are reflected and diluted versions of those derived from urban centers — often, it is true, conservatively resistive to the changes that occur in those urban centers whose hinterland they occupy.

Now it seems also true that such peasantries are the main source of labor migrating into the growing towns and cities — as pressure on the land or other social disturbances become acute in the countryside. Once in the town and cities these rural migrants are transformed into proletariat — though of course not overnight. Roots in the countryside are maintained at least for the migrant generation and whenever possible many such urban migrants return to the countryside either for short visits or permanently. Similarly when new emigrants from the country come to the city they tend to cluster with kin or village mates who preceded them to the towns.

Not only do the rural migrants tend to remain in touch with their rural origins; they tend also to perpetuate the patterns of high fertility, once they have established their families in the town.

As we said earlier, demographers have produced a considerable body of material on differential birth rates in rural and urban populations. There is some literature which I wish I knew better than I do but from what I do know of it one of the most widely accepted propositions in this field is that birth rates in cities are lower than in their rural hinterlands. However, when more refined social categories are used and differential fertility rates *within* cities are scrutinized this generalization breaks down. For example, in Irene Taueber's recent report on Hong Kong, given at the Association for Asian Studies, it became clear that urbanism is not per se the most significant variable but rather that a low woman-child ratio is directly linked in the Hong Kong study — as I'm sure in other studies — to higher educational levels, to higher economic status and to later marriages. These observations are commonplaces to most of you here and have already been stressed. It is not the rural-urban contrast, not the simple fact of industrial employment, but rather access to what Mrs. Taueber has called the "modernization complex" which determines birth rates.

But what is this modernization complex, so powerful that it can alter the fertility patterns of a social group? Clearly it entails profound cultural and social changes — changes in the meaning and the values given to human existence and the conditions under which life seems worth living. Culturally, for example, it may mean that a Hindu father no longer sees his postmortem security vested in having at least three sons so that he will be sure to have one surviving male heir to perform the annual memorial service after his death. Socially it means that the economic returns of both the peasant and the proletariat are sufficiently large and sufficiently assured that child labor no longer seems an economic necessity. It means that health conditions are adequate enough to insure the survival of the majority of the young, instead of only perhaps 50 per cent as is the case in many countries. Above all, it means a social structure that provides peasants and proletarians access to a higher standard of living and a greater satisfaction of material wants.

In other words, this modernization complex is the revolution of rising expectations. It is in fact a deep alteration in the society and in the culture of a population aggregate. Such a revolution is a multi-dimensional phenomenon. Family planning is not a "thing" in itself. It is only an aspect of what some people call westernization, some industrialization, some urbanization, but which more properly we should call modernization.

It is not just that men hear that there is a population explosion and something must be done about it and decide to regulate their reproductive behavior accordingly. Such a mentalistic approach to human behavior is sheer nonsense. Human behavior is based on an intricate blend of calculated self-interest, unquestioned assumptions, of patterned behavior and role relationships and of emotional spontaneities. Man's ego mechanisms are both expressive and defensive but they are also adaptive. He will change as his opportunities and his environment change. He will adopt family planning if he sees it as adaptive.

In sum, the modernization complex, the revolution of rising expectations, economic development, and a political system that permits a more equitable distribution of goods are all intricately meshed. This is the revolution that is changing the face of the contemporary world. Family planning and the control of population growth must be seen as part and parcel of this nexus.

Now, I warned you earlier that I would brashly argue a strategy of population control. You have patiently heard me out on my reasoning and it is clear that I can no longer delay outlining what seems to me the most effective procedure for introducing the knowledge and the means of population control to peoples. At a macro-social level the health services and the legislation are clearly necessary. But they are not in themselves sufficient. One must use the strategic points of departure and follow the channels of influence.

There is an old saw which I believe should not be disregarded by those who are initiating programs of change alluded to by Professor Parkes: "Nothing succeeds like success." And I would reverse G. B. Shaw's wit and say, "Nothing fails like excess."

I believe that action programs for family planning will be pursued most effectively and should be undertaken first in that portion of urban society which is experiencing the revolution of rising expectations, namely, the white collar category. This is precisely, of course, the procedure Dr. Freedman described for Taiwan. And I can assure you that I reached my formulation before I knew about the Taiwan project and that it was one reason I was so delighted to hear Dr. Freedman's talk. But at the same time that this action program is launched, careful research should concern itself with the access provided the proletariat to comparable modernization and also the channels of communication between those already prepared to accept family planning, namely the white collar society, and those urban dwellers who have not yet caught up on the "modernization complex." The second phase of action would then be aimed at the proletariat while the second phase of research would be to look into the channels of communication between town and country. The third phase of action would be the country itself.

Now, if there is any virtue in this suggestion of phased and related action and research, the implication is clearly that a frontal attack on the two great reservoirs of population increase may not be the best way to go about spreading knowledge of family planning. Rather, an oblique attack may prove more feasible, more enduring and far less expensive.

To repeat, action — that is, making available means of controlling birth rates and persuading people to use them — should be pursued in three successive stages: to the "white collar society," to the proletariat, to the peasantries. Simultaneously, research to facilitate the next phase of action should be preparing for the successful implementation of such action.

Now, in all of this the mountain has labored and brought forth its mouse. I would like to stress some additional and disparate points: I enter them as a series of caveats simply to advise you that I am not quite so simple-minded as the sketchy procedures I have just been outlining might suggest.

1) Research inquiries must be broad-gauged. They must go well beyond mere attitude testing and descriptions of demographic situations. There must also be in any such action and research program provisions for feeding research findings back into the planning scheme before the next phase of action is undertaken. We all know how often this is not the case.

2) Another point that I would like to stress, and it is one that has already been made by Dr. Freedman, is that an action program need not be seen as covering a whole population. As I said earlier, I am convinced that although the ultimate success of population control may well have to have its macro-social aspects, the real heart lies in the micro-social aspects. It lies in the primary group, the face-to-face relationships. Therefore action programs are best geared to the breeding population and if knowledge of birth control methods are needed and persuasion is indicated, they are probably best addressed to men and women who have just had a child and who may therefore be

more receptive to controlling subsequent births. This procedure reduces vastly the requirements for personnel and organizational facilities. I'll be most interested to hear the results of the Taiwan study on this score and I will hazard the guess that most mass media serve no persuasive purpose although they may have a little value in advising those already persuaded where to find the information they already want.

3) It is ill-advised, it seems to me, in many countries — some Catholic ones for example — to make a political issue of family planning programs. This is using a sword where a scalpel is needed. In such countries by far the best tactics would be to stress health and welfare programs and a host of other factors involved in this modernization nexus and let desire for birth control come of its own.

4) There are undoubtedly some countries where population control is not an issue. For example there is one where officials, (I had the name of the country and tactfully took it out) repeatedly report seeing their lusty population grow over 3 percent per annum as no source of concern at all since there is still much land for the peasantry to move out into. Here I have only one and possibly an impractical suggestion to make, and that is that foreign aid be definitely contingent on the willingness to disperse industrial establishments, thereby providing employment and nascent urban centers adjacent to the heavily breeding peasantries — increasing their resources and providing them a possible focus of potential change, and a channel of communication into cities. This is clearly a selective process, a matter of astute and very particular diplomatic negotiation, certainly not anything that can be written grossly into national policy.

5) Another point that certainly is important and that has been glossed over here is that towns and cities cannot be treated as a single variable. They vary tremendously in their functions and in their relationships to the countryside and therefore in their draw-

ing power for migrant labor. This question involves us in the murky and still unsatisfactory question of the typology of towns and cities. I think this is a fascinating subject and a resolvable problem, but it is certainly one tangential to our immediate interests here today. I would not consider it for a moment tangential, however, to a program of joint action and research in population control, when the nature of the city in which you are working and the function it serves in relation to the countryside becomes a crucial matter.

6) A sixth issue, certainly not explored here, is that communication between white collar, proletarian and peasant societies ·may prove to be either minimal or nonexistent. I can cite areas in which I believe such a situation exists. For example in some Latin American countries the Spanish, Ladino and Indian populations do not represent an interlocking social structure but three socio-cultural populations living together symbiotically. There is no interpenetration, or a minimal amount. Where such conditions exist it becomes necessary to treat each socio-cultural population as though it were, as indeed it is, separate and impermeable. The revision of strategy in such a situation would be to begin in each population with that group that has made the greatest stride towards the "modernization complex."

7) I am also quite aware that activists will say that my oblique and phased attack on the problem is self-defeating, that the situation will be out of hand before such a phased program could be successful. I agree with such fears, but I can think of no alternative for an effective reduction of population growth that promises at least to be enduring and effective in its successes. Although I realize that there is every urgency, we probably do have about a generation of leeway. Though these pros and cons and their implications were most interestingly argued by Dr. Coale there can be no doubt that the sooner we get

started, the better. Japan, whose rationality on the subject of population control and whose whole process of modernization provides possibly the best example in the world of national policy on these scores will have taken almost a century to stabilize its population if prognostications are correct. The control of population growth — for reasons I have already discussed — is not a quick, one-shot affair. We should not delude ourselves. Many of the field projects whose purposes Dr. Wyon has already so well summarized represent no more than a useful but preliminary learning about the problem of population control. They are vastly instructive but they must still be hitched effectively to action.

8) Let me enter an eighth and final caveat — one that is inevitably levelled in drawing-room conversations on a scheme such as I have suggested. My suggestion, I need hardly repeat, deals with exploiting readiness for family planning among an "elite" experiencing the opportunities of modernization. When this suggestion is raised in drawing-room conversations with precisely those modernizing "elites," the common reply is: "But this is encouraging the breeding of undesirable elements of the population at the expense of ourselves, that is, the desirable elements." I cannot deny this. During the century it may take, with concerted intelligence and effort, to persuade the great reservoirs of breeding populations that it is in their own interest to reduce the woman-child fertility ratio, a vast replacement of population in social categories will probably occur. After all we have managed such replacements in social categories in the United States and without too much anguish. This is not however the equivalent of saying that cultural values will have been lost. And it is man's culture (his capacity to give meaning to life) rather than man's society (his capacity to aggregate) that makes him supremely human.

If man lives by society alone he may resemble the self-destructive lemmings who go overboard, who over-breed and throw themselves into the sea. If man lives by culture, despite the threat of population growth, he may, but just may, avoid a senseless self-extermination.

My topic is not the intricacies of man's virtues and vices, nor the threat of atomic war. It's the question of population growth in socio-cultural terms. I think that my ethical position has become clear. I prefer social flexibility to cultural abnegation or biologic extermination.

DISCUSSION

Dr. Levin opened the meeting for discussion of Dr. Du Bois' paper.

DR. HOAGLAND: I would like to point out that the human brain is an organ of survival. It has been developed by biological evolution by the same processes of natural selection that has produced the fighting teeth, claws and horns of animals and thick protective integuments. The human brain has been exceedingly effective as an organ of survival. The brain is only secondarily an organ for discovering truth and for the things we intellectuals do with it. Therefore the appeal to self-interest and to personal advantage for a couple to limit the number of children they have makes good sense biologically.

S. J. Patel in the November Bulletin of the Atomic Scientists has pointed out that during the past ten years the world has spent something like 12 hundred billion dollars on armaments. This is more than we have spent on all of education in the 300 years since the Renaissance. The world expenditure of 120 billion per year is equivalent to over ⅔ of the national incomes of the underdeveloped countries, equal to about 8 to 9 per cent of the world's annual output and close to the value of the world's export of all commodities. Patel points out that if this 1200 billion dollars spent over 10 years had been used to raise the industrial accomplishments of underdeveloped countries, we would have something like 12 times the industrial development of these countries that we have now. The past ten years' expenditure on arms would have produced something like a 300 per cent increase in the per capita income of everyone in these countries. It has been suggested that it may not be possible to do very much about controlling the populations in underdeveloped countries until we have disarmament and use the funds thus freed to increase the educational levels and prosperity in these countries to a level where the people are sufficiently relieved from poverty and illiteracy and ignorance to a point where they wish to limit their families and are able to use suitable techniques to do so. The question arises that if we did have disarmament and are now spending 10 per cent of our gross national product on arms, would we use a substantial amount of this for raising living standards in the underdeveloped countries? Certainly there would probably be much opposition from Congress. Nevertheless, with a disarmed world, I'm sure that we are going to continue to have intense industrial and social competition with the USSR. This competition in peaceful coexistence would challenge us to use a very substantial part of what might be saved on military hardware in these directions, and the Soviet Union would match this competition in underdeveloped countries, so there is a fair likelihood that there would be a substantial flow of support into these countries following major disarmament. This might raise levels of aspiration to the take-off point of population control.

H. R. ATKINSON: There is one very broad and general question that I would like to ask Dr. Du Bois and that is: in respect to relying entirely upon cultural evolution, doesn't that disregard the genetic and eugenic aspect that develops this "organ of survival" that Dr. Hoagland has just stressed? For instance, in regard to the future, to try to utilize the inheritance of the Ph.D.'s, the stars, and many others. She didn't touch on that element. She touched on the question of "how many?," but left the question of "who?" aside, trusting that there would be no loss involved in relying solely on cultural ties. I don't know if that is a very clear question, but it does raise the eugenic angle of the future.

DR. LEVIN: I shall not try to repeat the question. Dr. Du Bois.

DR. DU BOIS: This is a question I can't answer, except that I have never known nor does any eugenist or any human geneticist know if there is any genetic relationship, or any relationship in human populations between class and genetics.

MRS. RULE: I'll take a stab at it.

DR. DU BOIS: Good. Thank you.

MRS. RULE: I would like to mention the fact that the inheritance of intelligence is a result of multiple alleles. In other words, there is not just one gene for intelligence, but many. It would seem because of this fact that there is a reservoir of genes for intelligence in the tribal, peasant, and proletarian elements that you mentioned. The gene reservoir would be equal for this group and the probabilities that they would show or express themselves would be just as great in these classes as in the middle class or the aristocracy which you mentioned. The problem with intelligence is namely that it is also behavioral, in other words, the genes for these potentialities probably exist in these populations right now, but do not express themselves by our cultural definitions or tests. Thus, a lack of certain socialization processes rather than a lack of the proper genes is present in certain classes and societies. Thus, if the middle classes and upper classes had a decrease in population, then this would tend to bring about a reduction in the population on all levels once attitudes and knowledge disseminated throughout the society. It might bring about an extension of the middle class and perhaps, a change in the total class structure. Thus, a reduction in the birth rate in the upper classes would be to the benefit of mankind.

DR. DU BOIS: Thank you for answering that so much more competently than I could have.

DR. PLANK: In one attempt to determine whether such differential fertility really resulted in a type of negative selection, it was found that school children in Scotland from large families had lower IQ's than those from small families. It was obvious to the eugenists that this differential would lead to a population with lower IQ's in the next generation. So they went back with expectations of showing this a generation later and found that IQ's were actually higher. I think what has just been pointed out is certainly true: that the provision of education and other opportunities is going to have a greater impact on the achievement in the society than is the questionable deleterious effect of selection against aristocratic genes.

DR. LEVIN: Are you suggesting that the IQ changes?

DR. PLANK: What is measured by the tests. Yes.

DR. GEOFFREY VENNING: I think the question of the intelligence of people in the rural areas is very important. They're not stupid and when provided with effective methods of contraception which are accessible to them, there doesn't really seem to be an insurmountable barrier. It may not be necessary to wait until such time as they have been organized and modernized. In fact, where trials of this kind have been carried out practical progress has been made. For instance, in Madras state, the spread of the means of contraception which is not linked with the act of intercourse, namely vasectomy, has gone up quite rapidly in the rural areas. Reports in the last year show that half of these operations were done at the primary health centers in the rural areas. Now this didn't require modernization and industrialization in such areas. It just depended upon activity at the periphery. I think the key to population control is the encouragement and support of the people actually working in the periphery rather than limiting financial support to the top government levels.

DR. LEVIN: Dr. Du Bois, do you want to respond?

DR. DU BOIS: If someone else wants to respond, it would be much better. I've made my point.

DR. FREEDMAN: I'd just like to add that we have a good many examples of other efforts in India and Pakistan where the effect has not been the one that is reported for Madras. I don't know that particular example but we have at least a half a dozen, probably closer to a dozen, instances in which contraceptives were provided in rural areas, and they were not effectively used. I would endorse strongly the point of view that Dr. Du Bois expressed. I think that it is obvious from the point of view I expressed yesterday. I would like to add that there are quite a few examples of efforts that have failed in rural areas where it was just the question of bringing the word to the people. Now I wouldn't insist that they would always fail and I'm sure there must be special circumstances under which they would succeed, but I think it is a very difficult task. I would like also to endorse very strongly the point that Dr. Du Bois made about classifying urban areas in cultures, and taking different approaches to them. I think that the role of education for example is very different in different situations. She cited the Hong Kong example, and I cited the Taiwan example where we have illustrations of the relationship between education and fertility and family planning. The relationship is very different in Western countries now. For example, in the United States at the present time, except for the very lowest stratum (and that's getting very small) of people, those who have had only a grade school education, there is practically no differential as between the different educational groups. Part of the explanation of this is just the reverse of the point that Dr. Du Bois was making about Hong Kong. She was saying that you can translate the rural urban differentials into educational differentials. We have, for the United States, indications that you can do just the reverse, that is that many of the educational differentials in fertility to which we have historically attached a lot of importance are really rural differentials. That is the people with poor education were mainly rural migrants. We have a number of series for both the national population and for some of the cities in the United States which indicate that education no longer makes very much difference as long as the populations have not had a farm background.

DR. TIETZE: I heartily agree with what Dr. Freedman has said about the great difficulties and lack of success of projects in rural areas. Having just returned from Pakistan, I'm very much impressed with the importance of paying more attention to the cities. The principle of starting the family planning program in the urban areas is embodied in the official documents concerning the scheme, but in practice far too many people tend to run off into the villages where the work is so much more romantic and so much less dirty than in urban slums. One of my strongest recommendations was that a great part of the effort should be spent on the urban areas. If I understand Dr. Du Bois correctly, her urban white collar class excludes the poor clerk who has no savings and lives from hand to mouth. If thus the urban white collar class is limited to the professional, managerial and technical occupations, it will be found that at least some of the Asian countries are now in the second phase of Dr. Du Bois' scheme. In these countries, the urban white collar classes, more narrowly defined, are already practicing family planning or family limitation. The next step is the extension of the practice into the urban proletariat. We are a little bit ahead of the game.

MR. DYSON: One of the things that has pleased me tremendously is how over the last few days we have been trying to introduce several disciplines to one another and link our thoughts. And I'd like to follow through a little on this if I might. I'm very much encouraged by what Dr. Du Bois said and also by what was said previously from the point of view of economics. There are one or two points I'd like to touch on showing how the use of this intellect we've all been paying homage to, can lead us to go further and point out some of the things I think we have to look at.

There are some linkages between this very point of rising expectations and the economic concept of consumption, and of course between these and population control. Earlier, for instance, the question was asked, "What about the United States and our growing unemployment?" We tend to look at this with our own cultural myopia. When Dr. Du Bois spoke of culture, she said, "We must learn to think how the Indian thinks." We should also learn how we think because our culture conditions how we approach him. In terms of the United States when we think of unemployment, we think automatically of impoverishment when actually if you look at the trend in the United States, we have been moving steadily since the 'thirties toward legitimate methods of removing people from the economy as producers yet continuing their economic ability to consume. We've been doing this through the Social Security mechanism of government, industry, and private enterprise, by keeping children in school longer and even by such means as the Peace Corps, foreign and domestic, which some say is another method of removing people legitimately from our working force. But, the key point here is that we have provided them with a consumption base so that in other words even though they are not producing, they are still consumers. Ever since the 1930's we have been looking unconsciously at people economically, not as producers but as consumers. The basic problem we face is not rising unemployment but the ability to continue consumption.

Yet because of our own cultural viewpoint, we use a double standard when we look at the developing countries. We are living under an economy where consumption is the key to how to use our industrial capacity; it serves the growth of capital too. Yet when we go to India or to Africa or the rest of the developing nations, we tend to go back to our Puritan cultural heritage and say, "We must form capital by production," whereas we are using consumption as our own key. Now Dr. Du Bois mentioned that another of the keys has been to move down and modernize the lower classes; part of this of course, is to help them to move into a cash economy. In Latin America they are trying to move forward land reform. Again, we think of food production. Actually what is happening, but we tend not to recognize it, is that we are moving these people into a cash and consuming economy on which their industrial formation and capital formation is built.

Thus, I would like to make a plea that when we talk of modernizing these other nations, in terms of their economics, we think not just in terms of production but in terms of consumption. Of course this immediately raises the question, how can we develop mechanisms by which they might speed up their consumption? At this point again according to our culture we don't like to see giveaways. But land reform in particular is essential, whether it's a give-away or not. Also on this point of raising consumption there has been a very interesting recent study done in Mauritius. If you think anything I've said so far is a little different, this will be more so. The key part of the Mauritius study, already implemented by legislation, done in 1959 or '60 by Tithuss and Abel-Smith of the London School of Economics, deals with social welfare policy and population. As part of the answer to population control they have built a social security system into this Indian Ocean island, and one of the reasons for it is to build up the general consumption levels in order to meet aspiration levels and in that way modernize and move more quickly towards population control.

DR. HARKAVY: I should like Dr. Wyon and Dr. Freedman to comment on Dr. Du Bois' assertion that family planning propaganda and information in mass media is relatively ineffective. This position, incidentally, is supported by Dr. Arne Kinch, director of the Sweden-Ceylon family planning pilot project, who asserts that one must reach the woman on a person-to-person as soon as she has had a baby. If one is to start family planning programs among urban and presumably more literate groups wouldn't the mass communications media serve as a useful reinforcement for the person-to-person approach? I am reminded that in Japan the use of women's magazines are alleged to be effective carriers of family planning information to a highly literate population.

DR. DU BOIS: Let me remind you of a distinction which I did make and I said that I thought the mass media were useful to inform people where they can get advice and help when they are already persuaded but that mass media are not in themselves persuasive. So I think we must talk to these two distinctions and now I would like to hear what Dr. Freedman and Dr. Wyon have to say.

DR. FREEDMAN: I think I would go a little farther than Dr. Du Bois did in regard to the point that Bud Harkavy made on the side of reinforcement. One of the things which we found out in Taiwan is that while those large proportions that I gave you yesterday are in favor of doing something and expect to do it, a large number of women are afraid that their neighbors don't think that way. And there are obviously some hesitations and I would think that the mass media for a population that is literate would have a reinforcing effect. One of the things we are trying to do is to follow the advice that Dr. Du Bois has given with respect to feedback. We have been using the results of our first pilot study for newspaper stories in which we are telling the people in Taichung, "It is alright — your neighbors think the way you do." We are extremely interested to see if that makes any difference. It is also true that we have a high proportion of thought to evidence. We don't have much evidence and we need research. We are trying this out in a small way in Taichung and we need a lot more evidence. I certainly agree that it is unlikly that it will do the job by itself. I would think that it would have more of an informative value where the population is ready.

DR. DU BOIS: That may very well be true. Yes.

DR. LEVIN: Dr. Wyon, would you like to comment?

DR. WYON: Before making any comments, I must make a confession. Luckily I was given a little warning of what Dr. Du Bois was going to say through Mr. Dhillon who was talking over this subject with Dr. Du Bois recently. He had roughly outlined to me the suggestions that Dr. Du Bois has made. The confession is this: I am one of those romantic rural people; my experience is with village people; my immediate reaction was that all this primary emphasis on urban people was ridiculous, but I have been turning the proposal over since then, and would like to see Dr. Du Bois' suggestions tested. I have great faith in the rural people, and hope that one day this faith will be justified. I think that Dr. Tietze's point was unquestionably right, that many poor people in India, and this is my very strong though unproved impression, are already having small families by deliberate action. When it comes to the next point of dealing with the proletariat, it seems to me that we come up against some pretty hard facts. The Family Planning Association of India started birth control clinics in India. There have been many clinics in Bombay for 10 or 12 years. The Delhi municipal family planning clinics have been going for several years, I cannot say exactly how many years, at least 4 or 5, and the apparent fact is that so far these clinics, as they are run now, make little impact on the urban proletariat. The number who attend the clinics is 1 per cent or less of all the couples in the city. But at the same time studies such as those which have been done in Calcutta by Poti and others indicate that some of these people are already practicing birth control. The methods used include *coitus interruptus* (interestingly enough in view of the history in Western Europe and the United States) and this seems to be one of the methods most commonly and effectively used. So my caution here would be to take seriously our experience of five years in a village situation in which birth control was used by some 20 per cent of the couples where the wife was of child-bearing age, yet without any noticeable effect on the crude birth rate. I think we should warn ourselves that even under the best conditions working among the proletariat, we are probably in for another five years of work before we start to see any results on the crude birth rate. But this does not disvalue the sense of Dr. Du Bois' general argument. During the five years working with people of the proletariat type it will make tremendously good sense to establish connections with their rural family relations.

Now as regards the person-to-person contacts of visiting people when they have just had a baby: this is one thing we tried to the best of our ability in the villages of the Khanna Study. We took special care to put the matter of child spacing and birth control to women just before the birth of their baby. We visited their husbands. The same procedure was followed when the baby was about 6 months old. I think it is a good idea. We found that many of the people in the rural area said "I have natural spacing, I shall not conceive until I start menstruating again." So again we went for these crucial points about the time when they started to menstruate; but apparently without any special effect. So I should support Dr. Freedman's suggestion of discussing in small groups, to ensure that the people all share in approving the idea of birth control. But I think we have a lot more basic research to do before we really find out the things which are the key to getting people to be determined to have only small numbers of children.

GENERAL DISCUSSION, CLOSING SESSION

Dr. Levin opened the meeting for general discussion.

VICTOR MC ELHENY: I just want to make it known that there is one newspaper man present — with all these comments about mass media. It is obvious from the efforts made by people concerned that population problems do get into the papers, at least in the United States. There is a certain amount of usefulness in the mass media in getting agreement on policy, at least on our own part. Also, I think, the newspaper business and magazines have confessions of failure to make in understanding the actual impact, the actual role that they do have in societies. I think their socio-culture role is very poorly understood and we probably ought to do a lot more about it.

JOHN MARSTON: Listening to the discussion on the sociological aspects of a campaign for contraception, I felt that Dr. Du Bois was quite right in concluding that, at present, we must concentrate on the cities. However, in many countries the rural population has the greatest proportion of reproductive activity and contributes most of the reproductive explosion; I don't think we can dismiss it as being beyond help.

The trouble with almost all the methods of contraception in use today is that they are so tedious, and often require such skill and determination in use that they become very inefficient. Some of the methods are too expensive for simple rural communities; but surely the main reason why contraception is not accepted by these communities is that it is far too great a "labor of love."

The new intra-uterine contraceptive devices are extremely effective and require absolutely no attention once they are properly in place. They seem to be safe and acceptable to most women. These devices could be very widely used in a rural community, no matter how primitive. I think we should imagine a program of contraception which would be led by a small nucleus of medical specialists, but staffed by adequately trained lay technicians. Such a service should be linked with a proper public health service, the rudiments of which already exist in most countries. It might depend on a village midwife for public relations work, particularly in helping women to continue their period of post-parturient infertility with effective contraception. The veterinary artificial insemination programs operate in several underdeveloped countries with great success, and yet they faced just as many "sociological" problems as any contraceptive program.

Even the simplest rural community will soon realize when Mrs. Brown, Mrs. Smith and Mrs. Jones haven't had any children for two or three years that a contraceptive can work. We might see a catalytic effect with a "contraceptive explosion" matching our present population explosion.

DR. VENNING: I seem to have been out on a limb listening to the ideas about rural areas. I would like to describe a couple of what I would call sociological feedback mechanisms, one a negative feedback and one a positive feedback. The negative feedback mechanism applies when methods of contraception are used but are not effective amongst the population to whom they are offered. I think this explains the widely observed failure of the family planning movement to expand. If you have a method and only about 20 per cent of the women like it, or are willing to use it, in the circumstances in which they live, then the corollary is that the other 80 per cent go tell their friends that this family planning movement is a waste of time. This goes back to the idea that the simple, uneducated people are not stupid. They're very sensible; they recognize that the methods that they have been offered are not suitable for them and they tell everybody else. This is the negative feedback. Now, the other is a positive feedback. If I may go back to the Madras vasectomy program, the number of vasectomies done (the number down there is 100,000, not 10,000) and if you look at the sequence of the number of these, the slope of the curve is remarkably like the slope of the population curve; it is an exponential rise. They set a target of 20,000 in 1962 and they did 50,000. And the 25,000 in the rural areas has involved a large number of people for a small number of operations and some of them have only started within the last few months. There is every reason to believe that the use of methods which are effective provides a positive feedback, a forward feedback. The same thing has happened in many of the oral contraceptive trials. The latent period seems to be about 18 months or two years. Then when there are enough people around to know that the method works, the thing snowballs.

I would like to make a final comment about rural programs; one of the most striking features about progress in general economic development in India is that a big effort is being made in the rural areas. It seems to me that it would be logical to include education in family planning with high priority in the public health program (which is largely rural) rather than to regard it as a specialized function of specialized people. This is how it is being done in Madras State where vasectomies are performed by Medical Officers in primary health centers in rural areas. I don't see why family planning couldn't take its place in a rural program along with agricultural development and so on. *I don't agree at all with the view that others have expressed that the major efforts in family planning and population control should be directed to the cities.* I think it is essential that further efforts should be made and financial support given in those areas in the periphery where effective action is already being taken.

DR. HENRY VAILLANT: I would like to ask Dr. Venning if he has available the number of children on the average fathered by these men who come for vasectomy. In other words do people come for vasectomy having had five or six children, or do they come earlier in the game?

DR. VENNING: If they come too late in the game, it may not do much good, as far as population growth is concerned. In Madras they have set the level a little lower with a limit of three. They don't do vasectomies for people with only two children.

RONALD L. NUTTALL: I was somewhat puzzled that nobody so far in this seminar has mentioned an issue which is very important in many questions of population control and this is the political and the power question. I am certainly not competent to discuss it but I hope that somebody will. We have a situation where there are different nations in the world and there are people who consider that, especially with nationalism as manifested as it is, they consider an increase in the population as an aid and not a harm. And I think that this is an important factor, not only between nations, but within nations where we have two or more disparate population groups within a nation, either cultural, racial or ethnic. There's often a population competition and perhaps somebody will discuss this as a population problem.

DR. LEVIN: Any volunteers to discuss this question?

DR. HOAGLAND: I might comment on the experiences I had at a 1961 Pugwash Conference involving American, Russian and European scientists. The question came up as to what East and West scientists could do to cooperate on aiding problems of world food supply and how we could work together constructively. I pointed out that linked with this problem was the problem of population control and that these two couldn't be separated. But the Russssians said that we couldn't talk about this profitably and that such a discussion would end in an empasse. The reason we couldn't discuss it is that according to the communist view, science and technology, under the Marxist system, will be able to feed everybody and therefore there is no point in restricting populations. So we didn't discuss this topic since you have to talk about things you can talk about. However, in the past two years the Soviet position has changed and they are more inclined to recognize the magnitude of the population problem, and apparently China also is concerned today. It certainly ought to be. I think that in many of the European countries that used to feel as Mussolini did, that one had to have large populations to become soldiers, this idea has become obsolete because we know that future wars aren't going to be fought by masses of infantry to any significant degree.

DR. LEVIN: Thank you, Hudson. This is probably the point at which we should stop the discussion now in accordance with the program. Since I am the last of the nonorganizers who will appear before you perhaps you will permit me to voice for you — and certainly for myself — our gratitude to the Committee which organized this conference, to the American Academy of Arts and Sciences which sponsored it and to the Ford Foundation which provided financial support. I think we all agree that the conference was superbly organized and carried off. I should like to express my personal hope that the Committee and the Academy will see fit to hold repeat conferences in the future. Thank you all very much.